Ethnicity and Mental Health

Findings from a National Community Survey

JAMES Y NAZROO

POLICY STUDIES INSTITUTE
LONDON

The publishing imprint of the independent
POLICY STUDIES INSTITUTE
100 Park Village East, London NW1 3SR
Tel. 0171 468 0468   Fax. 0171 388 0914

ISBN 0 85374 718 0
PSI Report 842

The Fourth National Survey of Ethnic Minorities was undertaken in partnership by
Policy Studies Institute
Social and Community Planning Research

It was supported by
Department of Health
Department of the Environment
The Joseph Rowntree Charitable Trust
Economic and Social Research Council
Department for Education and Employment/Employment Service

Cover design by Andrew Corbett
Laserset by Policy Studies Institute
First printed in Great Britain by BPC Wheatons, Exeter
Reprinted in 1999 by Athenaeum Press, Gateshead, Tyne & Wear

0164827

Ethnicity and Mental Health

This book is due for return on or before the last date shown below.

CANCELLED

0 8 MAR 2007

2 4 APR 2007

1 1 DEC 2007

- 3 MAY 2000

19 FEB 2002

CANCELLED

CANCELLED

CANCELLED

12 MAR 2003

- 1 NOV 2004

1 MAR 2001

CANCELLED

2 1 MAY 2005

26 APR 2001 0 4 JUN 2005

14 MAY 2001

CANCELLED 0 5 OCT 2005

- 3 NOV 2005

JUN 2001

1 3 FEB 2006

London, N.21   Cat. No. 1208

DG 02242/71

Contents

Foreword

The British medical profession only developed an interest in culture and ethnicity during the period of Commonwealth migration that effectively ended in the 1970s. 'Culture' has seldom been a variable factored into the discussion of psychiatric illness among White Britons who have always been taken as the reference group for calculating the rates of mental illness; by comparison, other groups – in the past generally migrants – have had their levels of illness considered as relative to the natives and explained by their 'culture' as causing higher or lower rates of illness. The PSI study is most welcome in beginning to unpick this assumption in suggesting that an examination of 'culture' (often for doctors a proxy for some rather biological idea of 'ethnicity' close to earlier ideas of 'race') might reveal the status of minority groups in Britain in terms of differential class status and patterns of marriage.

Until now, our figures for mental illness in different groups in Britain have been derived from the numbers actually treated in hospitals and clinics. But how does this reflect the figures for illness 'out there', unrecognised by doctors and untreated? We have paid little attention to the ease or otherwise by which people from different ethnic communities have entered the mental health care system. How are different problems recognised? What is the appropriate way of seeking help? Is psychiatry stigmatised and to be avoided at all costs? How visible is mental illness to the agents of surveillance in our society – doctors, social worker, police and courts? How much of what to doctors is mental illness is perhaps a response to interactions between the potential patient and the doctor? We can attempt to solve these problems by doing community surveys of people in their own homes, although surveys like this still have their own biases in the training of the researchers and one's reticence in disclosing intimate details of thoughts and feelings to a stranger calling at the door. Nevertheless the results of community surveys are essential if we are to balance the accounts collected in medical facilities.

One of the intriguing and most welcome findings of the PSI study is that the alarmingly high rates of psychosis among people of Caribbean origin in Britain seem much less when measured in the home by members of the same ethnic group than when they are assessed by white psychiatrists in the hospital. And this opens up a demand for future study to look at how institutions like prisons and psychiatric units might enhance the figures of pathology. Not so reassuring is the previously unknown frequency of depression and suicidal thoughts among Caribbeans – and that they appear to see their family doctors for these difficulties but do not receive any treatment.

If 'culture' has been usually ascribed to some hypothetical zero point of origin, it is noteworthy that Caribbeans born in Britain or who migrated here when young, are twice as likely to be anxious than older migrants, and seven times more likely to have suicidal preoccupations; and that a higher class status does not protect them in the way it does for the White Britons. And similarly anxiety among those of South Asian origin seems more common among those fluent in English.

Is there any convergence in the patterns of mental illness between different groups? It is noteworthy that British South Asians who have generally been felt to escape severe mental illness, do have, if they are British born, rates approaching the white rate. Models of experiencing and expressing psychological difficulties do still have differences which for want of a better term we might term 'cultural'. The study readily admits the difficulties of assessing minor illness through the use of Western questionnaires which are translated in the expectations of having the same meaning in another language and ethnic group. The researchers here point out the difficulties of translating words like 'depression' and assuming that an approximation will have the same meaning. Very differently from most medical surveys (although the dropping of the somatic section of the Clinical Interview Schedule is to be regretted), the PSI readily acknowledges these difficulties. We might regret the absence of more culturally-sensitive tools but a comparative study requires the use of a fairly single set of ideas and measures which can be approximately used in the groups to be compared.

For the present these measures are those of European psychiatry. We can only look forward to the reverse procedure by which minority concepts such as the Punjabi 'sinking heart' are operationalised and used in questionnaires for White Britons. And then we can perhaps argue for or against the universality of these and other medical categories. Until then *Ethnicity and Mental Health* provides us with a closer approximation to the reality of psychological illness among minority groups than we have previously been able to obtain. I commend it enthusiastically.

Roland Littlewood
Professor of Anthropology and Psychiatry,
University College London

Acknowledgements

This volume is one of a series based on the Fourth National Survey of Ethnic Minorities. A follow-up study on diagnostic issues related to mental health, which provided a crucial grounding for this report, was funded by the Department of Health. The Fourth National Survey itself was jointly sponsored by the Economic and Social Research Council, the Department of Health, the Department of the Environment, the Department for Education and Employment with the Employment Service, and the Joseph Rowntree Charitable Trust.

An expert group advised the research team on the mental health elements of the study. It was chaired by *Richard Berthoud* and its members were:

Paul Bebbington (University College London Medical School)
Dinesh Bhugra (Institute of Psychiatry)
Terry Brugha (University of Leicester)
Liza Catan (Department of Health)
Eleanor Cole (The Maudley Hospital)
Jenny Griffin (Department of Health)
Sanjay Gupta (Department of Health)
David Halpern (University of Cambridge)
Glyn Harrison (University of Bristol)
Sushrut Jadhav (University College London Medical School)
Glyn Lewis (University of Wales College of Medicine)
Keith Lloyd (University of Exeter)
Howard Meltzer (Office for National Statistics)
Dele Olajide (NHS Executive)

The advisory group made contributions throughout this study, helping with the training of interviewers, commenting on and contributing to the analysis as it proceeded, and providing detailed comments on earlier drafts of this volume that led to significant improvements.

Apart from this formal group of advisers, the work on the survey benefitted from advice and commentary from a large number of friends and colleagues in universities and research institutes, in government and elsewhere.

The research itself was undertaken in partnership by the Policy Studies Institute and Social and Community Planning Research. PSI had primary responsibility for the overall structure of the study, and for this book. SCPR was responsible primarily for the design of the survey, and especially the sample; and for the massive tasks of data collection and preparation.

At Social and Community Planning Research, *Roger Jowell* held overall responsibility for the SCPR end of the partnership. *Patten Smith* and *Gillian Prior* undertook the primary role in managing the Fourth National Survey, and *Gillian Prior* managed the follow-up part of the study.

A number of people at the Policy Studies Institute contributed to this volume. *David Smith* was originally responsible for getting the project off the ground and led the team through the design phase before taking up a chair at the University of Edinburgh. *David Halpern* was responsible for the development and design of the health element of the questionnaire and of the follow-up study. During the fieldwork he left PSI for Nuffield College Oxford and then the University of Cambridge but remained in close contact as a member of the advisory group. Following David Smith's departure, *Richard Berthoud* took the overall responsibility for the study and made important contributions to all stages of this volume, including the analysis and interpretation, before leaving PSI to take up a chair at the ESRC Research Centre on Micro-Social Change (University of Essex). Other PSI staff who made significant contributions to the study included *Chris Maynard* (data analysis), *Siân Putnam* (administrative support), *Karin Erskine* (typesetting) and *Jo O'Driscoll* (publications).

All of these people and organisations contributed to the research. But above all we are grateful to the 8000 people who took part in the survey and provided information about their experiences. Responsibility for this report, and its conclusions, lies with the author.

Acronyms and Abbreviations

CIS-R	Clinical Interview Schedule
ECA	Epidemiological Catchment Area
GP	General Practitioner
ICD	International Classification of Diseases
NACRO	National Association for Care and Resettlement of Offenders
OPCS	Office of Population Censuses and Surveys
PSE	Present State Examination
PSI	Policy Studies Institute
PSQ	Psychosis Screening Questionnaire
SCAN	Schedules for Clinical Assessment in Neuropsychiatry
SCPR	Social and Community Planning Research

CHAPTER ONE

Introduction

BACKGROUND

The relative prevalence of mental illness among different ethnic groups in Britain is probably one of the most controversial issues in the health variations field. Much of this controversy has focused on the apparently high rates of schizophrenia and other forms of psychosis among the African Caribbean population. Evidence suggesting low rates of mental illness among the South Asian population, but high rates of suicide and attempted suicide among young South Asian women, has also caused controversy.

This volume presents the findings of a detailed study of the prevalence of mental illness among ethnic minority groups in Britain. It is based on interviews with 5196 people of Caribbean or Asian origin, and 2867 whites, followed by a more detailed clinical examination of those who appeared to show symptoms of mental illness. Before the detail of the study is described, issues relating to ethnicity and mental illness will be considered.

Ethnic minority groups in Britain

The 1991 Census was the first to collect information on the ethnic origin of the population of Britain. Previously information had been collected on country of birth, but in 1991 the Census asked people to identify which ethnic group they considered themselves to belong to. Findings from this suggested that about 6 per cent of the population of Britain were members of non-white groups, i.e. about three million people. The Census also showed the diversity of the origins of ethnic minority people. Of the three million people who identified themselves as non-white: 27 per cent said that they were Indian; 16 per cent were Pakistani; 6 per cent were Bangladeshi; 22 per cent were Black–Caribbean or Black–Other (who appear to have been predominantly British-born Caribbeans); 7 per cent were Black-African; 6 per cent were Chinese; and 16 per cent were Other–Asians or Other–Other. Of course these ethnic groupings remain somewhat artificial (a point discussed later in relation to this survey), an issue that is most clearly seen in the degree of ethnic diversity that must be included in the 'Black-African' group.

The 1991 Census was also able to show that there are important differences in the geographical locations of different ethnic groups. More than half of ethnic minority people lived in the South East, compared with less than a third of whites.

The metropolitan areas of the South East, West Midlands and West Yorkshire contained almost two-thirds of the ethnic minority population, compared with less than one in five of the white population. And when enumeration districts (the smallest geographical areas identified) are considered, more that half of ethnic minority people lived in areas where the total ethnic minority population was greater than 44 per cent (Owen, 1994). There were also differences between different ethnic minority groups, for example while large numbers of Black–Africans, Black–Caribbeans and Bangladeshis lived in inner London, many Indians lived in outer London and the West Midlands, and most Pakistanis lived in the West Midlands and West Yorkshire.

There are also important differences between the socio-economic positions of different ethnic minority groups. Table 1.1 uses data from the Fourth National Survey (Modood *et al.*, 1997) to show the distribution of ethnic groups across three indicators of socio-economic position: social class; unemployment rate; and quality of housing. It clearly indicates that Indian or African Asian (i.e. those Indians whose families spent some time East Africa) and Chinese respondents were in a similar position to white respondents, while Caribbeans, Pakistanis and Bangladeshis were, to varying degrees, worse off. More detailed evidence on this is presented elsewhere (Modood *et al.*, 1997).

Table 1.1   Socio-economic status

	White	Caribbean	Indian or African Asian	Pakistani	Bangladeshi	Chinese
						column *percentages*
Registrar General's Class						
I/II	35	22	32	20	11	40
IIIn	15	18	21	15	18	26
IIIm	31	30	22	32	32	20
IV	20	30	26	33	40	13
Weighted base	2364	1402	1856	618	190	334
Unweighted base	2239	1057	1772	856	406	187
Per cent of economically active unemployed	11	24	15	38	42	7
Weighted base	1727	1102	1308	405	123	257
Unweighted base	1603	814	1238	564	248	143
Per cent lacking one or more basic housing amenities[1]	16	17	16	39	32	19
Weighted base	2867	1567	2091	862	285	391
Unweighted base	2867	1205	2001	1185	591	214

[1] i.e. excluse use of: bath or shower; bathroom; inside toilet; kitchen; hot water from a tap; and central heating.

There are, of course, differences also in the context and time of the migration of different ethnic minority groups to Britain. Overall, then, it appears that studies of ethnic minority groups in Britain need to be sensitive to their cultural diversity and to the differences in the material contexts of their lives in Britain.

Mental illness

Although mental illness is a relatively common condition, it is difficult to measure. Both the definition and the measurement of mental illness depend on the presence of clusters of psychological symptoms that indicate a degree of personal distress, or that lead to behaviours that cause such distress to others. The clusters of symptoms associated with particular forms of mental illness are clearly defined (see, for example, American Psychiatric Association, 1995; WHO, 1992), although the elicitation of these symptoms for diagnostic or research purposes can be difficult, an issue that will be discussed in the context of this survey later.

For current purposes it is useful to divide mental illness into two categories, psychotic and neurotic disorders. The former are less frequent, but result in more severe disability. They are thought to affect around one person in 250 (Meltzer *et al.*, 1995) and typically involve a fundamental disruption of thought processes, where the individual suffers from a combination of distressing delusions and hallucinations. Delusions often involve some notion of being persecuted or that some external force is controlling the individual's thoughts, while hallucinations typically involve hearing voices talking about or to the individual.

Neurotic disorders are much more common than psychotic disorders. A recent national survey suggested that in the week before interview about one person in 16 was affected by such a disorder (Meltzer *et al.*, 1995). They are usefully separated into two categories, anxiety and depression that, although they are common, do involve considerably more than a sense of anxiety or sadness. For example, an individual with clinically significant anxiety would experience severe physical symptoms of anxiety along with some restriction in his or her social activity as a result of the anxiety, while an individual with clinically significant depression would be sufficiently sad and distressed to lose interest in most things and to be brooding on things to such an extent that she or he could not concentrate and could not sleep properly.

African Caribbeans and psychosis

Hospital based research in Britain over the past three decades has consistently shown elevated rates of schizophrenia among African Caribbeans compared with the white population. African Caribbeans are reported to be at least three times more likely than whites to be admitted to hospital with a first diagnosis of schizophrenia (Bagley, 1971; McGovern and Cope, 1987; Harrison *et al.*, 1988; Littlewood and Lipsedge, 1988; Cochrane and Bal, 1989; King *et al.*, 1994; Van Os *et al.*, 1996). This evidence has, on the whole, been interpreted in one of two ways by commentators. Many have accepted these data as broadly valid and regarded them as an opportunity to investigate the aetiology of schizophrenia. From this perspective, uncovering the reasons for the higher rate among African Caribbeans would help resolve issues regarding the causes of schizophrenia more generally (e.g. Glover, 1989; Sugarman and Crauford, 1994). The kind of explanations considered for the higher rates of psychosis among African Caribbeans are similar to those that are considered for other ethnic variations in health. However, as there is only limited evidence available beyond hospital admission rates, their relative merit can only be cursorily examined.

First, the different rates of schizophrenia could be a consequence of factors related to the process of migration. Social selection into a migrant group could have favoured those with a higher risk of developing schizophrenia, or the stresses associated with migration might have increased risks. There is evidence to both support and counter these suggestions. Investigations of the rates of schizophrenia in Jamaica and Trinidad suggest that they are much lower than those for African Caribbeans in Britain and, in fact, similar to those of the white population of Britain (Hickling, 1991; Hickling and Rodgers-Johnson, 1995; Bhugra *et al.*, 1996). This would suggest that the higher rates are either a consequence of factors related to the migration process, or of the circumstances surrounding the life of ethnic minority people in Britain. However, if the higher rates were a consequence of migration, we would expect other migrant groups also to have higher rates. Evidence here is contradictory. On the whole studies have suggested that other migrants to Britain, in particular South Asians, do not have similarly raised rates (Cochrane and Bal, 1989). But, King *et al.* (1994), in a unique prospective study of all ethnic groups coming into contact with health and social services in a region within London, found that the incidence rate for first onset schizophrenia was higher in all ethnic minority groups compared with the white population.

In addition, if the higher rates were a consequence of selection into a migrant group or the stresses associated with migration, one would expect the rates for those born in Britain to begin to approximate those of the white population. However, studies have suggested that rates of schizophrenia for African Caribbeans born in Britain are even higher than for those who migrated (McGovern and Cope, 1987; Harrison *et al.*, 1988), suggesting that factors relating directly to the process of migration may not be involved. Although these data (like most work in this area) are dependent on a very small number of identified cases.

As with all work on ethnicity and health, there is the possibility that differences may be a consequence of some factor inherent to ethnicity. Although cultural factors are implicated in the notion of ethnicity, beyond speculation they have not been directly considered in research. Differences in biological risk might also be an explanation for the higher rates. However, the evidence cited above, which showed that there were important differences between African Caribbeans who stayed in Jamaica, those who migrated to Britain, and those who were born in Britain, suggests that the higher rates are not a straightforward consequence of genetic differences. It has also been suggested that the rates of schizophrenia among African Caribbeans are at their greatest for the cohort born in the 1950s and 1960s, and that this may be a consequence of exposure to a particular prenatal hazard among women newly arrived in Britain, such as an infection unfamiliar to the mother's immune system (Glover, 1989). If this was the case, we should be able to identify a clear cohort effect in the prevalence of psychosis among African Caribbeans.

The different rates might also be a consequence of the discrimination and racism that ethnic minority people face in Britain. This could be a result of the actual process of discrimination and harassment, or a result of the social disadvantages that they lead to. There has been recent evidence of both the nature and extent of the harassment ethnic minority people are subjected to (Virdee, 1995; 1997), and it would not be surprising if the multiple victimisation that some are subjected to led to mental distress. It also would not be surprising if the poor, run down, inner city environments and poor housing that many ethnic minority people live in, and their poorer employment prospects and standards of living (Modood *et al.*, 1997), led to greater mental distress (King *et al.*, 1994). As elsewhere in the ethnicity and health field (Sheldon and Parker, 1992; Nazroo, 1997), there has been considerable criticism of the failure to take into account explanatory variables related to social disadvantage in work that links ethnicity to poor mental health, as there is a strong possibility that these confound the relationship (Sashidharan, 1993; Sashidharan and Francis, 1993). These authors suggest that ignoring the possibility that the relationship between ethnicity and health is a consequence of social disadvantage allows the theoretical alignment of psychiatric disorder with ethnicity. The suggestion that psychiatric disorder is a consequence of some inherent and stable characteristic of certain ethnic minority groups, a suggestion that is rarely empirically tested, then leads to the cultural and biological heritage of those groups becoming pathologised.

However, an approach that explained the higher rates of psychosis as a result of discrimination, harassment and other forms of social disadvantage would have to be reconciled with two pieces of evidence. First, evidence from the Fourth National Survey (Modood *et al.*, 1997) indicated that Pakistanis and Bangladeshis were the most disadvantaged ethnic minority groups, but they do not appear to have higher rates of any mental illness (Cochrane and Bal, 1989), although the evidence on their rates of mental illness is not conclusive. It is possible, however, that the particular and different ways in which ethnic minority groups are racialised could lead to different outcomes for different groups (Jenkins (1986) provides an example of this in relation to employment). Second, it is also puzzling to note that rates of anxiety, depression and suicide are lower among African Caribbeans than among the general population (Cochrane and Bal, 1989; Gilliam *et al.*, 1989; Soni Raleigh and Balarajan, 1992; Lloyd, 1993). (Although the most recent mortality data rates suggest that those born in the Caribbean have a similar rate of suicide to the general population (Soni Raleigh, 1996)). If greater exposure to various forms of social stress was the explanation for higher rates of psychosis, we would expect these more common outcomes of stress also to be more frequent in the African Caribbean population.

Despite the consistency of research findings showing that African Caribbeans have higher rates of psychosis, some commentators have not accepted the validity of these data and continue to suggest that a higher incidence remains unproven, arguing that there are serious methodological flaws with the research that has been carried out. (See Sashidharan (1993) and Sashidharan and Francis (1993) for comprehensive reviews of the problems with existing data.) In summary, these flaws particularly result from the reliance of most work on hospital admission data, which raises a number of linked problems:

- Until the 1991 Census, where a question on ethnic background was asked for the first time, there had been only limited and unreliable data on the size of the African Caribbean population from which hospital admissions are drawn, resulting in its possible underestimation and consequent overestimation of morbidity rates. It has also been suggested that this may also be a problem with estimates based on the 1991 Census, because ethnic minority people may have been under-enumerated (OPCS, 1994). However, some have shown that even if the African Caribbean population was much larger than they had estimated, the rate of psychosis would still remain significantly greater than that in the white population (Harrison *et al.*, 1988; King *et al.*, 1994; Van Os *et al.*, 1996).

• It is also possible that the number of African Caribbeans admitted to hospital with a first ever episode of psychosis could be overestimated. Lipsedge (1993) suggests two ways in which this might happen. First, because of the differences in the ways that African Caribbean and white patients are treated by mental health services (as described below), African Caribbeans may be more reluctant to disclose any previous psychiatric treatment. Second, high geographical mobility in this population might lead to records of previous admissions being missed. Both of these would result in studies of first contact with psychiatric services for psychosis overestimating the number of African Caribbean patients.

• Given that not all of those with psychosis are admitted to hospital, it is also possible that the data reflect the differences in the pathways into care for different ethnic groups, which result in African Caribbeans being more likely than equivalent whites to be admitted. In support of this possibility there is a large body of evidence that suggests that African Caribbeans (and other black people) are over-represented among patients compulsorily detained in psychiatric hospitals and are more likely to have been in contact with the police or other forensic services prior to admission. This is despite them being both less likely than whites to display evidence of self-harm and no more likely to be aggressive to others prior to admission (Harrison *et al.*, 1989; McKenzie *et al.*, 1995; Davies *et al.*, 1996).

• It is also possible that differences in the attitudes of health care workers to different ethnic groups and difficulties in the diagnosis of schizophrenia may be involved. For example, McKenzie *et al.* (1995) showed that African Caribbeans with psychosis were less likely than equivalent whites to have received psycho-therapy or antidepressants, and Harrison *et al.* (1989) showed that although African Caribbeans were no more likely to have been aggressive at the time of admission, once admitted staff were more likely to perceive them as potentially dangerous both to themselves and to others. Coupled with difficulties in diagnosis, these pieces of evidence suggest that the stereotypes that inform the behaviour of heath care workers may make them more likely to diagnose African Caribbeans as psychotic.

• In addition, some have argued that the symptom profile for Caribbean schizo-phrenics is different from that for whites and that they should be more accurately considered as having an atypical psychosis (Carpenter and Brockington, 1980; Littlewood and Lipsedge, 1981). However, both Harrison *et al.* (1988) and Harvey *et al.* (1990) showed that there were great similarities in the profiles of Caribbean and white patients with psychoses.

Interestingly, very similar criticisms have been made of epidemiological work in the United States (Adebimpe, 1994). Taken together, these comments suggested that there are a variety of potential problems with existing work and, consequently, that there must remain some doubt about the higher rates of psychosis reported among African Caribbeans. Indeed, although the study that is widely regarded as the strongest in this field (Harrison *et al.*, 1988; 1989) overcame a number of these problems – it adopted a prospective design that included all African Caribbean patients making first contact with both hospital and community based services, used a standardised clinical assessment to overcome potential biases in diagnosis, and used a similar general population survey as a comparison – it, inevitably, still contained significant methodological weaknesses that raised doubts about the validity of the conclusions drawn (Sashidharan and Francis, 1993). For example: the population denominators were indirectly estimated using 1981 Census data on country of birth of the head of household; the comparison group was not concurrent and, because it was identified on the basis of possible diagnosis while the African Caribbean group was identified by screening for ethnicity, there were important differences in case identification; and case identification was also dependant on identifying patients with first contact with psychiatric services, which has the problems described above.

South Asians, mental illness and suicide

Rates of mental illness among South Asian populations appear, on balance, to be lower than those for the general population (Cochrane and Stopes-Roe, 1981; Cochrane and Bal 1989; Gilliam *et al.*, 1989). However, these findings are not entirely consistent, some studies of overall psychiatric hospital admission rates suggest that South Asians have similar rates of admission (Carpenter and Brockington, 1980; Dean *et al.*, 1981). These lower rates also may not be consistent across type of disorder. Although rates of hospital admission for neurotic disorders are substantially lower than those for the general population (Cochrane and Bal, 1989), it seems that schizophrenia is equally or more common among South Asians than the general population, although not to the degree reported for African Caribbeans (Cochrane and Bal, 1989; King *et al.*, 1994). Also, while rates of suicide among most South Asians are equal to or lower than those of the general population, rates among young South Asian women are more than twice those of their white counterparts (Soni Raleigh and Balarajan, 1992; Soni Raleigh, 1996).

Given the comments made above about the types of social disadvantage faced by ethnic minority groups in Britain, the overall lower rates of mental illness among South Asians are puzzling. It has been suggested that the lower rates could be a consequence of a protective Asian culture, which provides extended social support networks, although others have criticised the stereotyped basis of such conclusions (Sashidharan, 1993). Indeed, in a small local survey in East London, MacCarthy and Craissati (1989) were able to show that levels of psychological distress were significantly greater for Bangladeshis compared with white respondents in similar situations. This led them to conclude that: 'the hypothesis that the Bangladeshi group would experience less distress, or be more psychologically robust in the face of adversity was not confirmed' (p. 200).

It is possible that the differences between white and South Asian groups, and the inconsistencies in these, could, like those for African Caribbeans, be a result of the methodological limitations of studies in this area. In addition to the difficulties of relying on treatment data, outlined above, the lower rates of mental illness among South Asians could reflect language and communication difficulties, or a general reluctance among South Asians to consult with doctors over mental health problems. More fundamentally, they may reflect a difference in the symptomatic experience of South Asians with a mental illness compared with whites. In particular, it has been suggested that South Asians may experience particular 'culture-bound' syndromes – that is a cluster of symptoms that is restricted to a particular culture – such as sinking heart (Krause, 1989), or may be more likely to somatise mental illness – that is experience and describe psychological distress in terms of physical symptoms (Rack, 1982) – and consequently not be identified as mentally ill.

Kleinman (1987), in what comes close to a relativist perspective on mental illness, has suggested that the problems with cross-cultural psychiatric research may be even more fundamental than this. Somatisation is typically seen as a result of a different, culturally informed, mode of expressing the 'same' disorder – that is a disorder with a similar biological basis. However, Kleinman (1987) suggests that the reliance on a biological definition of disease crucially undermines an understanding of how different the culturally shaped *illness* may be – differences in symptomatic expression reflect

> substantially different forms of illness behaviour with different symptoms, patterns of help-seeking behaviour, *course and treatment responses*... the illness rather than the disease is the determining factor. (p.450, emphasis added)

Given the reliance of psychiatric research on the identification of clusters of symptoms that reflect an underlying disease, Kleinman (1987) argues that cross-cultural research can easily lead to what he calls a 'category fallacy'. The use for research or treatment in a particular culture of a category of illness that was developed in another cultural group, may fail to identify many to whom it can apply, because it lacks coherence in that culture. This may, of course, be the case for instruments designed to detect western expressions of neurotic disorders when applied to other, particularly in this case South Asian, cultures. Indeed, Jadhav (1996) has been able to describe the historical and regional development of 'western depression', leading him to suggest that this apparently universal disorder is culturally specific.

There has only been limited empirical work in this area so there is only limited evidence to support this position. In one example, Fenton and Sadiq-Sangster (1996) identified an expression of distress that they described, using their respondents' words, as 'thinking too much in my heart'. While they found that this correlated strongly with the expression of most of the standard western symptoms of depression, they were also able to show that some of these standard symptoms were not present (those relating to a loss of meaning in life and self-worth), suggesting that at least the form that the disease took was different. They also pointed out that 'thinking too much in my heart' was not only a symptom as such, but a core experience of the illness, raising the possibility that there were more fundamental differences between this illness and depression.

As pointed out earlier, and in contradiction with the apparent lower overall relative rates of mental illness among South Asians, analyses of immigrant mortality statistics show that mortality rates from suicide are higher for young women born in South Asia, and this is particularly the case for very young women (aged 15 to 24) where the rate is two to three times the national average (Soni Raleigh *et al.*, 1990; Soni Raleigh and Balarajan, 1992; Karmi *et al.*, 1994). In contrast to the findings for young South Asian women, these studies also showed that men and older women (aged 35 or over) born in South Asia had lower rates of suicide. Analysis of the most recent data on immigrant mortality has been more detailed, because it could be coupled with the 1991 Census which asked a question on ethnicity as well as country of birth (Soni Raleigh, 1996). This confirmed the pattern just described, but was able to show that the high rates were restricted to those born in India and East Africa. Both men and women born in Pakistan and Bangladesh had lower mortality rates from suicide than the general population, while women born in India and East Africa had higher rates, and men born in India and East Africa had similar rates.

In the attempt to explain the high mortality rates of suicide among young women born in South Asia, research has explored the reasons given by those who have *attempted* suicide. Analysis of the hospital records of such people has focused on cultural explanations for attempted suicide and particularly on a notion of culture conflict, where the young woman is apparently in disagreement with her parents' or husband's traditional or religious expectations (e.g. Merril and Owens, 1986; Biswas, 1990; Handy *et al.*, 1991). Although, these reports are largely speculative, those who have extrapolated from them in order to explain the high mortality rates from suicide among young South Asian women have accepted such conclusions, locating the causes of these high rates outside individuals' mental health and saying that such instances of self-harm are a consequence of family pressures and conflict. For example Soni Raleigh and Balarajan (1992) state:

> Most immigrant Asian communities have maintained their cultural identity and traditions even after generations of overseas residence. This tradition incorporates a premium on academic and economic success, a stigma attached to failure, the overriding authority of elders (especially parents and in-laws) and expected unquestioning compliance from younger family members. Thus, interpersonal disputes particularly in relation to marriage and lifestyles, the pressures of economic competition with the loss of self-esteem associated with failure, and the anxiety attached to non-conformist behaviour have been cited as causes of self-harm among the young (male and female)... These pressures are intensified in young Indian women, given their rigidly defined roles in Indian society. Submission and deference to males and elders, arranged marriages, the financial pressures imposed by dowries, and ensuing marital and family conflicts have been cited as contributory factors to suicide and attempted suicide in young Indian women in several of the studies reviewed here. (p.367)

However, a closer examination shows that such stereotypes may not hold and there are, in fact, great similarities between the motives of white and South Asian patients for their suicidal actions. For example, Handy *et al.* (1991) say that arguments with parents were a common factor for both the white and Asian children in their study, and Merril and Owens' (1986) examples of 'restrictive Asian customs (e.g. not allowing them to go out at night, mix with boys, or take further education)' (p.709) are not greatly different from what one might find in a dispute between a young white woman and her parents. Indeed, a study of coroners' reports in London found that only one-third of the 12 South Asian women who had committed suicide had 'family conflict' cited among the reasons for the suicide, and only by stretching the imagination could these be considered as specific to South Asian cultures (Karmi *et al.*, 1994). As Lipsedge (1993) has pointed out, it is likely that:

> what would be described as 'parent-child conflict' among white families is 'anthropologised' by medical staff as clashes over cultural values rather than as personal difficulties or the everyday dynamics of family life... Thus culture itself becomes a form of pathogenesis. (p. 176)

Discussion

The review suggests that many basic questions concerning the relationship between ethnicity and mental health remain unanswered. There remains a question of whether the use of western psychiatric instruments for the cross-cultural measurement of psychiatric disorder is valid and produces a genuine reflection of the differences between different ethnic groups (Kleinman, 1987; Littlewood, 1992; Jadhav, 1996). This has been raised particularly in relation to the low detection and treatment rates for depressive disorders among South Asians, but may apply to other disorders and other ethnic minority groups. It is also possible that treatment-based statistics do not accurately reflect the experiences of the populations from which those in treatment are drawn. Two recent general reviews of the literature on ethnicity and mental health have pointed to the need for better data in this area, and particularly data derived from general population or community surveys (Smaje, 1995; Cochrane and Sashidharan, 1996). Finally, as others have pointed out (Sashidharan and Francis, 1993), from an aetiological perspective there is a need to explore the factors associated with ethnicity that may explain any relationship between ethnicity and mental health, such as the various forms of social disadvantage that ethnic minority people face. Once again, these can only be explored adequately within a community survey that includes both the ill and not-ill, so that the experiences of these two groups and how they vary by ethnicity can be explored.

However, a community survey to tackle these issues faces a number of problems. Any survey that intends exploring relatively rare events needs to be large and, as the recent National Psychiatric Morbidity Survey (Meltzer *et al.*, 1995) showed, psychosis is a rare event with a prevalence in the general population of around four cases per thousand people. In addition, because of the relatively small number of ethnic minority people in Britain (they make up about 6 per cent of the population according to the 1991 Census), and their concentration in particular locations within Britain (Owen, 1994), standard nationally representative samples inevitably contain too few ethnic minority people for any meaningful analysis to be carried out. For example, the National Psychiatric Morbidity Survey contained about 450 ethnic minority respondents within its total sample of almost 10,000 adults living in private households (Meltzer *et al.*, 1995). Finally, there remains the problem of measurement, such a survey would inevitably use a fully structured interview that could not even begin to be address cross-cultural issues.

The work reported here is based on the Fourth National Survey of Ethnic Minorities (Modood *et al.*, 1997) and a follow-up validation study based on a clinical interview. These presented an unique opportunity to carry out a community based survey that explored the relationship between ethnicity and mental health, and they have been able to overcome many, although by no means all, of the difficulties facing such research.

RESEARCH METHODS

Conduct of the surveys

During 1993/94 the Policy Studies Institute (PSI), in partnership with Social and Community Planning Research (SCPR), undertook a detailed survey of people from ethnic minority groups living in England and Wales – The Fourth National Survey of Ethnic Minorities. This built on the three earlier surveys carried out by PSI, which charted the changing position of Britain's ethnic minorities from 1966 to the present day. Ethnically and language matched interviewers undertook structured interviews with a sample of 1205 Caribbeans, 1273 Indians, 728 African Asians, 1185 Pakistanis, 591 Bangladeshis and 214 Chinese. For comparative purposes the survey also included 2867 white respondents, among whom there were 119 with Irish family origins and 94 with neither Irish nor British family origins. The assignment of individuals into particular ethnic groups used here is based on country of family origin. This process of assigning ethnicity is, of course, a complex and controversial process, which will be discussed in detail in a later section of this chapter.

As well as containing an extensive section on health (Nazroo, 1997), the survey covered many traditional measures of social and economic disadvantage, including sections on type and quality of housing, area of residence, employment and income, and education. In addition, two important new sections were added. The first covered ethnic identity, allowing a detailed exploration of ethnicity and how different ethnic groups view themselves and their lives in Britain. The second covered the incidence and experience of racial violence and harassment, including, for the first time in a national survey, the experience of 'low level' racial harassment. A discussion of these data can be found in Modood *et al.* (1997).

The health section of the survey covered six broad areas:

1 General health status – e.g. self-assessed health and which activities were limited by the respondent's health;

2 Cardiovascular disease;

3 Other specific physical health problems – such as diabetes and respiratory symptoms;

4 Health-related behaviours – such as smoking and drinking;

5 Use of health services – including hospital services, general practice, dentists, home helps etc., and covering aspects of the accessibility of these services to different ethnic groups;

6   Mental health – covering depressive and psychotic disorders (and described in full later).

A discussion of the findings from the first five of these areas can be found in Nazroo (1997).

Given the measurement problems outlined above and the necessary reliance on a fully structured interview for the Fourth National Survey, it was imperative to assess of the validity of the mental health measures used. This led to the development of a follow-up study, also carried out by PSI and SCPR, of those respondents whose answers suggested that they *possibly* had a mental illness. This involved such respondents undergoing a well-established detailed clinical interview undertaken by ethnically and language matched psychiatric nurses or doctors. Version 9 of the Present State Examination (PSE) (Wing *et al.*, 1974) was chosen for the psychiatric assessment in this interview as it had already been translated into most of the languages required. The follow-up interview was also extended to provide coverage of treatment and use of health services. In many ways the design of these studies followed that of the OPCS National Psychiatric Morbidity Survey (Meltzer *et al.*, 1995), although there are some important differences, which will be returned to later.

Sampling and response rates[1]

Great attention was placed on the sampling procedure to ensure that respondents recruited into the survey were fully representative of the communities from which they were drawn (see Smith and Prior, 1997, for full details). The areas used for sampling were selected on the basis of data from the 1991 Census on the ethnic minority population size in enumeration districts and electoral wards. For the ethnic minority sample they included areas with few ethnic minority people, a population that has been ignored by other regional and national surveys of ethnic minority groups. This ensured that the wards and enumeration districts used represented those where less than 0.5 per cent of the population were members of ethnic minority groups (low concentration), those where between 0.5 and 10 per cent of the population were members of ethnic minority groups (medium concentration), and those where more than 10 per cent of the population were members of ethnic minority groups (high concentration). Once the sampling points were identified, the Postcode Address File was used as the sampling frame to identify households to be screened for inclusion in the study.

Screening for ethnic minority respondents was carried out in the field. In areas with a high ethnic minority concentration, suitable ethnic minority respondents were identified by asking at all of the selected addresses. In areas with medium and low ethnic minority concentrations, screening was based on the technique of focused enumeration, a method that has been shown to provide good coverage of the targeted populations (Brown and Ritchie, 1981; Smith, 1996). This involves interviewers visiting every n[th] (e.g. 6th) address in a defined area and asking about the ethnic origin

---

1   Full details of the survey methods used for the intial structured survey can be found in its technical report (Smith and Prior, 1997). Additional details of the methods used in the follow-up clinical survey can be found in the appendix of this report.

of those living at both the visited address and at the n–1 (e.g. 5) addresses on each side of the visited address. Consequently, non-visited address are asked about at two visited addresses. If a positive or uncertain identification is made at either of the visited addresses for the non-visited addresses, the interviewer then goes on to visit them in person. In practice the detail of this procedure varied according to the ethnic minority concentration in the area to be covered. In areas of low ethnic minority density every tenth address was used for the focused enumeration process, while in areas of medium ethnic minority density, on the whole every sixth address along the street was designated for an initial visit, but in some areas with more concentrated ethnic minority populations every fourth address was so designated.

Any households identified in this way as containing one or more people with an ethnic minority origin were then used to obtain the ethnic minority sample. In order to maximise the efficiency of the sampling process, in households containing ethnic minority people two adults were selected for interview whenever possible. (If there were one or two eligible adults in the household all were selected, if there were three or more two were selected at random.)

To identify the white sample a more straightforward three stage stratified design was used. First, a sample of wards was drawn. Second, from within each selected ward a sample of addresses were identified from the Postcode Address File. Finally, interviewers selected one random eligible adult (rather than a possible two, as in the case of ethnic minority households) from within each selected address. The sample of wards was drawn to include both those that had a concentration of ethnic minority households above and below 0.5 per cent, according to the 1991 Census.

Response rates to both stages of the Fourth National Survey – the initial interview and the follow up validation interview – are shown in Figure 1.1 by broad ethnic group (South Asian groups are combined and the Chinese group was too small to be considered separately). Also shown, for comparison, are the rates for the National Psychiatric Morbidity Survey (Meltzer *et al.*, 1994). This shows that response rates for the initial interview were similar for the white and South Asian groups to this survey and the respondents to the National Psychiatric Morbidity Survey. However Caribbeans had a lower response rate at this stage. Because screening for the ethnic minority sample for the initial interview was carried out in the field, some basic demographic information on some ethnic minority non-respondents could be collected.[2] This suggested that non-response was related to both age and gender. In terms of age, for all ethnic minority groups younger people were more likely to not have been interviewed. When comparing those aged under 35 with those aged 55 or more, the young compared with the old group were between about 15 per cent more more likely, in the case of Bangladeshis and Caribbeans, to almost twice as likely, in the case of African Asians, to not have been interviewed. Differences in response rate by gender were not so clear cut. For the Caribbean and Indian groups men were more likely to not have been interviewed, for the African Asian and Pakistani groups there was no difference, and for the Bangladeshi group women were more likely to have not been interviewed. If both age and gender are considered, for all ethnic minority

2   The following discussion does not cover the Chinese group, which was too small to consider by age and gender, nor the white group, for whom there was no information collected on non-responders.

Figure 1.1   Response rate to the Fourth National Survey by ethnic group

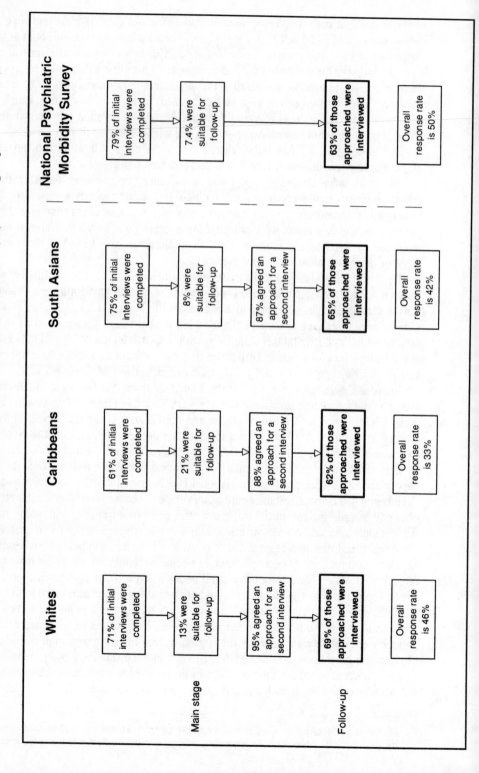

Figure 1.1   Response rate to the Fourth National Survey by inclusion criteria

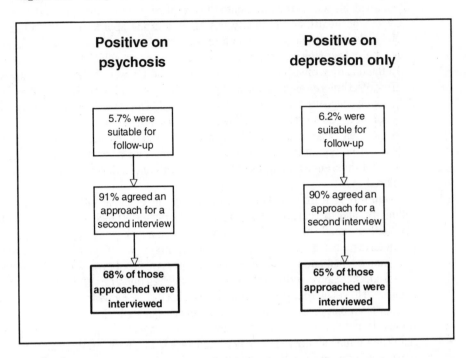

groups except Bangladeshis, young men were the most likely to be non-responders. Men aged under 35 compared with women aged over 55 were between about a third more likely, in the case of the Caribbean and Pakistani groups, to more than twice as likely, for the African Asian group, to not have been interviewed. For the Bangladeshi group, middle-aged men appeared to be the most likely group to not be interviewed.

For the follow-up interview, response rates were similar for all groups, although, as discussed later, the criteria for follow-up were different in this study compared with the National Psychiatric Morbidity Survey. The lower overall response rate for the Caribbean group compared with the others is entirely a result of their lower rate at initial contact. Figure 1.2 shows that the response rates for the follow-up interview for this study were not related to the reason for follow-up (the detail of the follow-up criteria is described later).

Finally, of the 35 per cent of respondents who we attempted to follow up and failed, only just over a third were outright refusals, the rest were the result of factors such as failing to make a second contact (see the appendix for more details on this).

Defining ethnic group

As Senior and Bhopal (1994) point out, the concept of ethnicity is by no means simple. It contains notions of shared origins, culture and tradition, and it cannot be considered as a fixed or autonomous feature in an individual's life. It has a dynamic relationship to both the historical and contemporary experiences of social groups and the individuals within them. Despite the complexity of the concept of ethnicity, most research on health and ethnicity has taken a crude approach to the allocation of individuals into ethnic groups. As a recent *British Medical Journal* editorial pointed out, the categories of ethnic group used in health-related research are often undefined and inconsistently used (McKenzie and Crowcroft, 1994). This allows the status of ethnicity as an explanatory variable to be assumed, treated as though objectively measured and, consequently, reified. The view of ethnicity as a natural division between social groups allows the *description* of ethnic variations in health to become their *explanation* (Sheldon and Parker, 1992), leading, as suggested earlier, to untested assumptions about the existence and importance of cultural and biological differences being asserted as fact without underlying explanations being explored.

One way forward would be to acknowledge the dynamic and contextual nature of ethnicity, and to research the relationship between ethnicity and health with this explicitly in mind (Ahmad, 1995). However, such a task is difficult, if not impossible, to undertake in a cross-sectional quantitative survey, which inevitably must rely on a one-dimensional and relatively crude measure. An alternative is to allow individuals to assign themselves into an ethnic group, which is the strategy adopted by the 1991 Census. However this suffers from a lack of stability, individuals often move themselves from one category to another when the question is repeated at a later date (Sheldon and Parker, 1992), a situation that is no doubt a reflection of the contextual nature of ethnic identity. The option used here is to ignore, on the whole, the role of perceived ethnicity and to assign ethnicity according to country of family origin. Not surprisingly, perceived ethnicity and country of family origin are highly related, as Table 1.2 shows.

Table 1.2   Self perceived ethnicity by ethnic family origins

column percentages

To which group do you belong?	White	Caribbean	Indian	African Asian	Pakistani	Bangladeshi	Chinese
White	99.8	0.3	0.5	0.1	0.4	0.3	3.3
Black Caribbean	0	83.7	0	0	0	0	0
Black African	0	1.1	0	0	0	0	0
Black Other	0	0.3	0	0	0	0	0
Black British	0	10	< 0.1	0	0	0	0
Asian British	0	< 0.1	0.8	0.8	0.6	0.3	0
Indian	0	< 0.1	96.9	88.2	0.3	0	0
Pakistani	0	0	0.6	6.0	98.3	0.2	0
Bangladeshi	0	0	0.2	1.0	0	98.8	0
Chinese	0	0	0	0	0	0	92.5
Mixed	< 0.1	3.6	0.8	1.7	0	0.3	2.8
Other	< 0.1	0.2	0.2	2.1	0	0	1.4
Not answered	0.1	0.7	0	0.1	0.4	0	0
Base	*2867*	*1205*	*1273*	*728*	*1185*	*591*	*214*

The approach based on country of family origin has the advantage of being a relatively straightforward and stable approach, although individuals within particular groups cannot be considered homogeneous in respect of a number of factors that may be related to both self-perceived ethnicity, such as religion or country of birth, and health, such as socio-economic status. The most obvious practical problem with this approach is how to deal with respondents who identify themselves as having mixed family origins. Here, a crude approach of wherever possible allowing ethnic minority status to override white status has been taken. Again, as Table 1.3 shows, this has only affected a small number of respondents in the South Asian groups and less than 10 per cent of those in the Caribbean and Chinese groups.

Table 1.3   Mixed ethnicity by ethnic family origins

column percentages

	White	Caribbean	Indian	African Asian	Pakistani	Bangladeshi	Chinese
				Ethnic family origins			
Those whose responses to family origins and group membership questions suggest mixed ethnicity	1.2	8.2	2.5	2.5	0.6	0.7	7.5
Base	*2867*	*1205*	*1273*	*728*	*1185*	*591*	*214*

For the analysis that will be presented later, some ethnic groups have had to be combined in order to have sufficiently large sample sizes. The way in which groups have been combined varies according to the type of analysis undertaken, in order to achieve a balance between sensitivity to differences between groups and the need for sufficiently large numbers of respondents with particular characteristics. Throughout the Indian and African Asian groups have been combined as their responses followed very similar patterns. In some cases the Pakistani and Bangladeshi groups have been combined, although where possible they have been kept separate. In the more detailed analysis it has been necessary to combine all four of the South Asian groups. Clearly such a combination leads to an unsatisfactory loss of detail about possible differences between South Asian groups. However, how the differences (and similarities) between these groups might influence the interpretation of data where they have been combined can be estimated from the earlier findings presented for individual groups. Throughout the Chinese group has been left uncombined, despite its small size, because it had a very different health profile to all of the other groups according to the other health assessments made in the Fourth National Survey (see Nazroo, 1997). This has meant that for some of the analysis this group could not be included. Where possible a white minority group has been used in the analysis. This includes respondents who said they had Irish family origins or that they were white and had family origins outside Britain. However, its small size meant that it could not be used for the more detailed analyses.

Assessing mental health

Initial assessment

The initial assessment of mental health used in the Fourth National Survey was based on structured questions. These were adapted from two instruments, the well established revised version of the Clinical Interview Schedule (CIS-R) (Lewis *et al.*, 1992) and the more recently developed Psychosis Screening Questionnaire (PSQ) (Bebbington and Nayani, 1995). The CIS-R is a standardised interview that covers neurotic disorders. It has been shown to be both a reliable and valid assessment of minor psychiatric disorder, and it has also undergone some cross-cultural validation (Lewis *et al.*, 1992). It was designed for use by lay interviewers – it consists of structured questions with the respondents' replies taken at face value – so in this sense is ideal for use in a study such as the Fourth National Survey. The assessment of neurotic disorders in the CIS-R is based on 14 symptom groups: somatic symptoms; fatigue; concentration and forgetfulness; sleep problems; irritability; worry about physical health; depression; depressive ideas; worry; anxiety; phobias; panic; compulsions; and obsessions. This allows the CIS-R to be used as both an overall assessment of disorder and to generate psychiatric diagnoses.

Although the CIS-R takes only 30 minutes on average to administer, this was far too long in the context of the Fourth National Survey. Two strategies were adopted to deal with this problem of length. First, only half of the ethnic minority respondents were asked the CIS-R schedule. Second, only certain of the 14 symptom groups were considered. Focus was particularly placed on depression, and all of the questions for the depression and depressive ideas symptom groups (except a question on interest in sex) were asked. In addition, many of the questions on anxiety, phobias and panic, and the introductory questions in the sleep and fatigue sections were asked. The most notable omission from the symptom groups covered were somatic symptoms. As discussed earlier, this is especially important as far as South Asian respondents were concerned, because somatisation may well be how some mental illnesses are experienced and expressed in these groups.

The use of a standardised interview carried out by lay interviewers for the assessment of psychotic disorders is widely felt to be considerably more difficult than for the assessment of neurotic disorders. A set of standard questions is probably too restrictive to assess psychotic disorders, as a lack of insight into the disorder may produce misleading responses to the questions asked. The alternative of a less structured approach to the assessment, with the interviewer making rating decisions, would require the interviewer to make clinical judgements and, consequently, she or he would need to have relevant clinical experience. For the Fourth National Survey, where such difficulties were impossible to overcome directly, the PSQ was used. This was designed as a screening instrument that identified whether there was *any* possibility of the respondent suffering from a psychotic disorder. For example, in a recent assessment of its performance among a sample of psychiatric in-patients, psychiatric out-patients and General Practitioner (GP) attenders, only 2 out 124 respondents who screened negative on the PSQ were found to have a psychotic disorder when they underwent a full diagnostic interview (using the Schedules for Clinical Assessment in Neuropsychiatry – the SCAN)

(Bebbington and Nayani, 1995). However, the use of such an instrument, while minimising the possibility of any false negative responses, does increase the false positive rate. The authors of the instrument suggest that if it is used in a population with a typical 1 per cent prevalence of psychotic disorder, for every six cases identified as positive by the PSQ only one would be a true case (Bebbington and Nayani, 1995). In order to further reduce the risk of false negatives, respondents to this survey were also asked about any medication they had used and any illnesses they had had diagnosed, so that those who had taken any antipsychotic medication or had been given a diagnosis of psychosis could be identified and followed up.

Validation of the initial assessment

For a number of reasons neither the CIS-R nor the PSQ could be used in a straight-forward diagnostic way. Although the CIS-R has been validated, only part of it was used here and it was not certain how the section used would perform. Also, while there has been some cross-cultural validation of the CIS-R, because of language and cultural differences doubts remain about the effectiveness of such standardised assessments of neurotic disorder for cross-cultural research, particularly for South Asian populations. The PSQ has only been validated as a screening instrument, and its deliberately high false positive rate clearly means that there are important limitations to its use in a diagnostic sense. In addition it has not had any cross-cultural validation.

In order to assess the validity of these measures, respondents who met broad criteria suggestive of possible mental illness were approached for inclusion in a follow-up survey that, as described above, involved them undergoing a detailed well-established clinical interview based on version 9 of the Present State Examination (PSE) (Wing *et al.*, 1974) and undertaken by ethnically matched psychiatric nurses or doctors. In an attempt to minimise the chances of missing any respondents who had a mental illness, the inclusion criteria used for the validation survey were as wide as possible. However, this does not mean that there were no false negatives and, as none of the respondents who were negative on all of the inclusion criteria were included in the follow-up, the full extent of this or whether it varied across ethnic groups cannot be assessed.

The detailed inclusion criteria for the follow-up were:

1   From the CIS-R, any of the following answers:

   a   Yes to 'Have you felt unable to enjoy or take an interest in things during the past *week?*'

   b   Four days or more to 'Since last week on how many days have you felt depressed?'

   c   Yes to 'Have you felt depressed for more than three hours in total on any day in the past week?

   d   No to 'In the past week when you felt depressed, did you ever become happier when something nice happened, or when you were in company?'

    e Yes to 'Thinking about the past seven days, have you on at least one occasion felt guilty or blamed yourself when things went wrong and it *hasn't* been your fault?'

    f Yes to 'During the past week, have you been feeling that you are not as good as other people?'

    g Yes to 'Have you felt hopeless at all during the past week, for instance about your future?'

    h Yes to 'In the past week, have you felt that life isn't worth living?'

2 From the PSQ,[3] any of the following sets of answers:

    a Yes to 'Over the past year, have there been times when you felt very happy indeed without a break for days on end?' *and* no to 'Was there an obvious reason for this?' *and* yes to 'Did your relatives or friends think it was strange or complain about it?'

    b Yes to 'Over the past year, have you ever felt that your thoughts were directly interfered with or controlled by some outside force or person?' *and* yes to 'Did this come about in a way that many people would find hard to believe, for instance, through telepathy?'

    c Yes to 'Over the past year, have there been times when you felt that something *strange* was going on?' *and* yes to 'Did you feel it was so strange that other people would find it very hard to believe?'

    d Yes to 'Over the past year, have there been times when you heard or saw things that other people couldn't?' *and* yes to 'Did you at any time hear voices saying quite a few words or sentences when there was no one around that might account for it?'

3 Reporting taking antipsychotic medication or having a diagnosed psychotic disorder

This allowed responses to the two sets of questions to be compared, so that the performance of the standardised questions in the main survey could be assessed and differences across ethnic minority groups could be analysed. This comparison will be the focus of the next chapter. However, before this is done, two of the limitations of the validation process are worth outlining.

First, the follow-up process involved a fairly complicated procedure. Once the initial interview had been undertaken, the coded data were entered onto a database. This was then immediately screened to see if the respondent met the follow-up criteria. The screening therefore was carried out on unchecked data and a small number of suitable follow-ups were missed and a small number of respondents were

---

3 Readers familiar with the PSQ will notice that one element, the question asking the respondent 'Have there been times you felt that a group of people was plotting to cause you serious harm or injury?', was not included among the criteria for the follow-up. This question was felt to be too problematic for use among ethnic minority respondents.

inappropriately followed-up. If the respondent did meet the screening criteria, his/her name and address was then passed on to the follow-up study's field managers. They then arranged for the original interviewer to introduce to the respondent an ethnically matched psychiatric nurse or doctor, with appropriate language skills, who then carried out the follow-up interview. The demands of this process meant that there was a certain amount of time between the two interviews. The median gap was 17 weeks, and 80 per cent of the follow-up interviews were done between 9 and 26 weeks of the first interview. Even though interviewers for the follow-up study were asked to question about the period relating to the original interview, the distance in time between the two interviews clearly could have implications for the validation process, especially in terms of the accuracy of the recall of symptoms. However, there is no indication in the data that there was a relationship between the length of time between the interviews and the likelihood to meet the criteria for a PSE CATEGO syndrome (which are described in full later) in this sample.

Second, the validation process for the cross-cultural assessment of mental illness involved more than simply checking the performance of the crude assessment compared with a more sophisticated assessment of psychiatric disorder. All of the interviews were carried out in the language(s) of the respondent's choice. The languages used included: Urdu; Punjabi; Gujarati; Bengali (Sylhethi); Hindi; and Chinese (Cantonese). For the initial assessment using the PSQ and CIS-R, translations of the questionnaires and other materials were carried out by a commercial translation agency and were checked by having the translation independently translated back into English. For the PSE, if translations were already available we used those, where they were not bilingual psychiatrists were asked to translate them. For this back translations were not carried out, but the flexibility that the PSE allows a clinically trained interviewer should have minimised any problems resulting from inaccurate translation. Consequently, in so far as the validity of the measures depended on the accurate translation of *questions* into alternative languages, we can be reasonably confident.

However, as Kleinman (1987) has pointed out, the reduction of issues around translation into a purely technical problem of finding equivalent words or phrases ignores the possibility that the underlying concepts may differ across cultures. All of the instruments used in this research are clearly developed from within a western psychiatry model, so will inevitably fail to detect non-western culture-bound syndromes, or symptomatic expressions of disease that are differently determined by non-western cultures. The only safeguard the study had here was the use of ethnically matched interviewers. Given the flexibility allowed interviewers in the validation phase of the study, the degree to which the interviewer and respondent shared a culture may have enabled them to be sensitive to different culturally-determined expressions of the same symptoms, even if different patterns of culturally-determined symptoms for the same disease could not be identified. Even so, this may have been limited by the training in western psychiatry that they had undergone.

Comparison with the National Psychiatric Morbidity Survey

At this point it is worth detailing the similarities and differences between the two elements of the Fourth National Survey and the National Psychiatric Morbidity Survey.

- Both the Fourth National Survey and the National Psychiatric Morbidity Survey used the PSQ (which was, in fact, developed for the National Psychiatric Morbidity Survey) and the questions on diagnosis or treatment of a psychotic disorder. Both studies followed up respondents who scored positive on these questions, with one exception (described next).

- An element of the PSQ – whether the respondent said yes to 'Have there been times you felt that a group of people was plotting to cause you serious harm or injury?' – was not included in the selection criteria for the follow-up to the Fourth National Survey, while it was for the National Psychiatric Morbidity Survey.

- While both studies also used the CIS-R, the Fourth National Survey only used part of it, with a particular focus on aspects relating to depression.

- Because of doubts concerning the effectiveness of western assessments of neurotic disorders among South Asian populations, the depression and depressive ideas elements of the CIS-R were part of the inclusion criteria for the follow-up validation interview in the Fourth National Survey. However, follow-ups in the National Psychiatric Morbidity Survey were only carried out on those who met one of the psychosis screening criteria.

- Finally, for clinical assessments the follow-up element of the Fourth National Survey used the PSE 9 together with additional sections on treatment and alcohol and drug use, while the National Psychiatric Morbidity Survey used the SCAN, which is constructed around the PSE 10.

OVERVIEW OF THE VOLUME

Chapter 2 of this volume is concerned with the validation process. It contrasts response to the CIS-R and PSQ with responses to the PSE for four broad ethnic groups: whites; Caribbeans; Indian/African Asians; and Pakistani/Bangladeshis. Comparisons between the different ethnic groups of the match between these sets of questioning gives some indication of the extent to which the CIS-R and PSQ behaved similarly across them and, consequently, how suitable the PSQ and CIS-R are for the ethnic comparisons made later in this volume.

Chapter 3 begins by using the validation findings to develop a scheme that allows an estimate to be made of the rates of depression and psychosis in different groups. It then goes on to show rates of mental illness by gender and age, focusing on anxiety, depressive neurosis, suicidal thoughts and non-affective psychosis. This provides the basic comparison between ethnic groups in rates of mental illness. The concluding section of this chapter explores the extent to which screening positive for mental illness was related to the use of medical services and how far this varied across different ethnic groups.

Chapter 4 takes the comparison between ethnic groups further by exploring the extent to which there were differences within ethnic minority groups according to age on migration and fluency in English, and what implications this has for the comparisons with the white group made in the previous chapter. Key issues covered include how far the work suggesting very high rates of psychosis among British born Caribbeans was replicated. The data are also used to obtain additional insights on the problems associated with a cross-cultural use of western psychiatric concepts.

Chapter 5 is concerned with exploring the impact of demographic and socio-economic factors on mental health variations within and across ethnic groups. It begins by exploring the degree to which rates of mental illness vary within ethnic groups by marital status and socio-economic factors. Then multivariate analysis is used to explore how far the demographic factors discussed in earlier chapters, and marital status and socio-economic position, were related to variations in mental health. Finally, multivariate analysis is used to explore the extent to which the ethnic variations in mental illness reported in earlier chapters were dependent on socio-economic and demographic factors.

Finally, the conclusion provides a summary of the context of the survey and the key findings presented in this volume. It then goes on to consider the implications of these findings for future research and policy in this area and for our understanding of ethnic variations in mental health.

CHAPTER TWO

Exploring the Validity of the Measures used

INTRODUCTION

This chapter is concerned with exploring the relationship between responses to the CIS-R and PSQ, used in the initial fully structured interview, and responses to the PSE, used in the follow-up clinical interview, and how this might vary across the ethnic groups included. It is important to remember that respondents who did not meet any of the CIS-R or PSQ criteria were not included in the follow-up. Consequently, little can be said about whether the initial questioning failed to identify some mentally ill respondents, and whether this varied by the ethnic origin of the respondents. As described in Chapter 1, both interviews were carried out by ethnically matched interviewers and in the language of the respondent's choice. However, the first interview was undertaken by 'lay' interviewers, whereas the second was undertaken by a psychiatric nurse or doctor who had received training in the use of the PSE.[1]

Table 2.1 shows the percentages of respondents who were suitable for follow-up according to each of the selection criteria (a respondent could, of course, meet more than one of the criteria). The data are age and gender standardised to allow for an immediate comparison of the ethnic groups.[2]

The most striking conclusion to be drawn from Table 2.1 is that all of the Asian groups were less likely than the white group to be positive on both the CIS-R (depression) criteria and the PSQ (psychosis) criteria. In contrast, the Caribbean group was slightly more likely than the white group to be positive on the CIS-R criteria and was twice as likely to be positive on the PSQ criteria. The greater risk of Caribbeans to be positive on the PSQ criteria held for all of its components.

---

1   After the interviewers had been trained on the PSE, their performance was assessed by asking them to rate taped interviews with a depressed and with a schizophrenic patient. The result of this exercise was satisfactory. Ratings of the depressed patient for all interviewers produced a CATEGO class (see latter for a description of this) of either neurotic or reactive depression. Ratings for just over three quarters of the interviewers for the schizophrenic patient produced a CATEGO class of simple schizophrenia, one-fifth of the interviewers' ratings lead to CATEGO class of depressive psychosis, and the remaining interviewer's ratings led to a class of non-schizophrenic psychosis.

2   These data do not show prevalence rates as only a proportion of those who screened positive actually turned out to be ill.

Table 2.1   Respondents suitable for follow-up by selection criteria

cell percentages: age and gender standardised

	White	Caribbean	Indian or African Asian	Pakistani or Bangladeshi	Chinese
Positive on CIS-R (depression) criteria	16.2	22.2	10.2	10.3	7.7
Weighted count	2867	783	1038	558	195
Unweighted count	2867	614	988	871	104
Positive on any PSQ (psychosis) criteria	5.5	10.8	3.3	2.5	1.9
Hypomania	0.4	0.7	0.2	0.1	0.0
Thought insertion	1.7	2.6	0.8	0.7	0.5
Strange experiences	3.6	7.5	2.7	1.7	1.4
Hallucinations	1.4	2.9	0.6	0.6	0.0
Positive on psychotic medication or diagnosis criteria	1.6	1.1	1.4	1.3	0
Weighted count	2867	1568	2903	1146	389
Unweighted count	2867	1205	2001	1776	214

When comparing the response rates to the follow-up shown in Figures 1.1 and 1.2 and the number of respondents suitable for follow-up shown in Table 2.1, with the number of respondents actually followed-up, as shown in the following tables in this chapter, some additional points are worth considering. First, because only half of the ethnic minority sample were asked the CIS-R (depression) screening questions, in order to give white and ethnic minority respondents an equal chance of being followed-up only half of the white respondents who met the CIS-R criteria were approached for the follow-up interview. Second, because the process of selection for follow-up took place before the data had been fully checked, not all of the suitable respondents in Table 2.1 were correctly identified and approached, and some unsuitable respondents were followed-up. Overall, 555 respondents were included in the follow-up and of these 24 did not meet the selection criteria.[3] Those who did not meet the selection criteria are excluded from the following tables.

THE ASSESSMENT OF MENTAL HEALTH IN THE FOLLOW-UP

The PSE, which was used in the follow-up, involves the interviewer making an assessment of whether or not a series of 140 possible symptoms are present. If any symptom is judged to be present, an assessment is then made of its severity. The CATEGO computer programme[4] can then be used to derive syndromes, categories,

---

3   Full details of the number of respondents at each stage of the study are shown in the appendix.

4   Here, rather than using the CATEGO programme, the symptom ratings from the PSE were entered into the SPSS-X statistical package. A programme was then written for SPSS-X that followed the CATEGO programme exactly and this was used to derive syndromes, categories, types and class.

types and eventually 50 hierarchical diagnostic classes. These 50 classes can be further reduced, using CATEGO criteria, to one of nine classes that include: schizophrenia; other schizotypal disorders; non-specific psychosis; psychotic depression; mania; depressive neurosis; and other neurosis. For the purposes of the validation exercise, the overall diagnostic process was considered in two stages.

First, the nine broad CATEGO classes were further combined to give three very broad hierarchical and mutually exclusive classes (described in descending order): a psychotic class (containing schizophrenia, other schizotypal disorders, and non-specific psychosis); a manic or psychotic depression class; and a neurotic class (containing depression, obsessional neurosis, anxiety and hysteria).

Second, the 38 syndromes, which the CATEGO programme directly derives from the symptoms rated by the interviewer, were combined in a direct way to reflect whether the respondent had any of the components of four broad symptom groups. These included syndromes suggestive of: psychosis; neurotic depression; anxiety; and other neuroses. The detailed contents of each syndrome group were:

1 *Psychosis* – nuclear syndrome, catatonic syndrome, incoherent speech, residual syndrome, depressive delusions, hypomania, auditory hallucinations, delusions of persecution, delusions of reference, grandiose delusions, sexual and fantastic delusions, visual hallucinations, olfactory hallucinations, non-specific psychosis, depersonalisation and sub-cultural delusions.

2 *Neurotic depression* – simple depression, affective flattening, features of depression, self-neglect, worrying, ideas of reference, lack of energy, irritability, social unease, lack of interest/poor concentration, other symptoms of depression.

3 *Anxiety* – general anxiety or situational anxiety.

4 *Other neuroses* – obsessional neurosis, overactivity, slowness, agitation, tension, hypochondriasis, and hysteria.

In contrast to the CATEGO classes, the CATEGO syndromes are a direct reflection of any and all symptoms reported by the respondent, so the programme naturally allows individuals to have more than one syndrome. This means that individuals are potentially counted in more than one syndrome group, but also means that none of the information on symptoms reported is lost, as it is in the hierarchical CATEGO class system.

Once the respondents in the follow-up study had been allocated into CATEGO classes and syndrome groups, comparisons could be drawn between the selection criteria for inclusion in the follow-up and responses to the PSE questions. The results of these comparisons are discussed next, although the small number of Chinese respondents included in the follow-up means that for this process they cannot be considered as a separate group.[5]

---

5 Many of the following tables include an 'All respondents' group. While this is useful for the validation process, it is important to recognise that differences in the sampling procedures for white and ethnic minority respondents means that this group is not in any sense representative of the general population. In order to draw conclusions about the usefulness of these instruments in the general population the white sample needs to be considered separately from the ethnic minority sample.

COMPARISON OF RESPONDENTS' CLASSIFICATIONS AT THE FIRST AND SECOND INTERVIEWS

As described earlier, recruitment into the follow-up was based on the respondent meeting the criteria for possibly having either a psychotic illness or a neurotic depression illness or both. As a starting point to exploring how effective the screening instruments were for different ethnic groups, it is useful to see how the selection criteria into the follow-up were related to the final diagnostic ratings made. Table 2.2 does this by comparing the selection criteria with the various combinations of CATEGO syndromes that the respondents were assigned to.

Table 2.2   Assigned CATEGO syndrome by criteria for selection into follow-up: all respondents

column percentages

	Selection criteria		
	PSQ (psychosis) only	PSQ and CIS-R (depression)	CIS-R (depression) only
Assigned CATEGO syndrome			
Psychosis with or without neurosis*	19 20	23	10
		79	
Any neurosis, no psychosis	47	67	66
None	34	10	24
Count	153	79	299

*   Very few respondents were assigned to a psychosis syndrome without neurosis, and the percentages here are reduced by less than 2 per cent in each column if those with only affective psychosis are not included.

The table shows that a number of respondents did not meet the criteria for any CATEGO syndrome. However, given our aim to reduce the number of false negatives as far as possible in the selection process, at the risk of a number of false positives, this would be expected. One-fifth of those who had screened positive for psychosis were found to have a psychotic syndrome (the top cells of the first and second columns combined). Four-fifths of those who screened positive for neurosis were found to have a neurotic syndrome (the four cells in the top right corner of the table combined). Both these figures are much as would be expected given the screening accuracies built into the PSQ and CIS-R respectively. However, 10 per cent of those who *only* screened positive on CIS-R (depression) criteria were assigned a psychotic CATEGO syndrome. This means that 30 out of the 73 respondents (41 per cent) who were assigned a psychotic CATEGO syndrome had not met the psychosis screening criteria. Similarly, 19 per cent of those who were assigned into a neurotic CATEGO syndrome were selected into the follow-up *only* on the basis of being positive on the psychosis screening. This raises the possibility that the screening was not as effective as we had hoped and that there were false negatives among the responses to the CIS-R and PSQ questions.

In order to explore the validation process further, the two selection criteria for the follow-up study will now be considered separately, although it is again worth bearing in mind that 15 per cent of respondents were positive on both criteria.

Validation findings for those positive on psychosis (PSQ) screening

Table 2.3[6] considers the CATEGO diagnostic class for respondents selected into the follow-up validation study on the basis of being positive on one or more of the PSQ (psychosis) items.[7] It shows a very similar pattern of response between the Caribbean and white groups, although slightly more Caribbeans were assigned a class of manic or depressive psychosis (this difference was not statistically significant). The Indian/African Asian and Pakistani/Bangladeshi, groups also had very similar patterns of response to each other. However, there were important differences between the two South Asian groups and the white and Caribbean groups. Although members of all ethnic groups were just as likely to be in a psychosis class, members of the South Asian groups were less likely to be in a neurotic class and more likely to fail to meet the criteria for any class. The differences between the white and the two South Asian groups in the 'neurotic' row were statistically significant.

Table 2.3   Assigned CATEGO class for those positive on PSQ (psychosis) screening

column percentages

	White	Caribbean	All South Asians	Indian or African Asian	Pakistani or Bangladeshi	All respondents (inc. Chinese)
Non-affective psychosis	11.4	14.1	14.3	11.1	18.2	12.7
Manic or depressive psychosis	2.3	5.6	2.0	0.0	4.6	3.3
Neurotic	64.8	60.6	38.8**	40.7*	36.4*	57.6
None	21.6	19.7	44.9	48.2	40.9	26.4
Count	*88*	*71*	*49*	*27*	*22*	*212*

*   p < 0.05 compared to the white group.
**   p < 0.01 compared to the white group.

A check on these findings is provided by Table 2.4, which looks at the distribution of CATEGO syndromes for those positive on the PSQ screening. Whereas the hierarchical ordering of CATEGO classes meant that psychosis took priority over neurosis, this does not occur with CATEGO syndromes, where all of the symptoms rated by the interviewer are considered and respondents are potentially being counted in more than one group.

In fact, Table 2.4 tells a very similar story to that told by Table 2.3. Whites and Caribbeans had a very similar distribution across the syndrome groups. The two South Asian groups also had a similar distribution to each other, but one that was

6   The percentages in Tables 2.3 to 2.6 are not indicators of the relative prevalence of mental illness, they are simply an indication of the relative validity of the screening instruments across different ethnic groups.
7   This does not include those respondents who reported taking anti-psychotic medication or a diagnosis of psychosis, but who did not meet the PSQ criteria.

again very different to that of the white and Caribbean groups. Despite having been just as likely to have a psychosis syndrome, they were less likely to have any of the neurotic CATEGO syndromes and more likely to have no syndrome. Again, the differences between the South Asian groups and the white group for the depression and anxiety rows were statistically significant.

Table 2.4   CATEGO syndromes for those positive on PSQ (psychosis) screening

	White	Caribbean	All South Asians	Indian or African Asian	Pakistani or Bangladeshi	All respondents (inc. Chinese)
Psychosis	20.5	22.5	18.4	14.8	22.7	20.3
Depression	75.0	73.2	51.0**	51.9*	50.0*	68.9
Anxiety	44.3	40.9	16.3**	18.5*	13.6*	35.9
Other	55.7	50.7	32.7	29.6	36.4	49.1
None	21.6	19.7	44.9	48.2	40.9	26.4
Count	*88*	*71*	*49*	*27*	*22*	*212*

*   p < 0.05 compared to the white group.
**   p < 0.01 compared to the white group.

Overall, Tables 2.3 and 2.4 suggest that in terms of the main aim of PSQ screening, that is identifying those at risk of having a psychotic diagnosis or symptoms, the instrument is successful. It gave a very similar result for all of the ethnic groups considered. Although only one in eight respondents in fact met the criteria for a non-affective psychotic CATEGO class (one in six if affective psychosis is included and one in five if syndromes are considered), it is worth recalling that the PSQ was designed as a screening instrument that had as few false negatives as possible, even if that meant greatly elevating the number of false positives. In contrast, if neurotic CATEGO classes and syndromes are considered, differences between the ethnic groups appear. Whites and Caribbeans had similar patterns, with about three out of five meeting the criteria for a neurotic CATEGO class and only one-fifth having no CATEGO class, but all of the South Asians were less likely to be in a neurotic CATEGO class and more than two-fifths of them did not meet the criteria for any class.

Validation findings for those positive on depression (CIS-R) screening

Tables 2.5 and 2.6 consider respondents who were included in the follow-up validation study on the basis of being positive on one of the CIS-R (depression) criteria. Table 2.5 gives the distributions for the hierarchical CATEGO classes for these respondents. Again, the white and Caribbean groups had a very similar distribution across the classes. However, members of the Pakistani/Bangladeshi group were considerably less likely than those in the white group to be assigned a neurotic CATEGO class and more likely to have no CATEGO class (and these differences were statistically significant). Members of the Indian/African Asian group were also less likely than those in the white group to be assigned a neurotic CATEGO class, although this difference was not statistically significant.

Table 2.5   Assigned CATEGO class for those positive on CIS-R (depression) screening

column percentages

	White	Caribbean	All South Asians	Indian or African Asian	Pakistani or Bangladeshi	All respondents (inc. Chinese)
Non-affective psychosis	7.5	9.5	9.7	10.6	8.5	8.5
Manic or depressive psychosis	2.7	0	2.7	3.0	2.1	2.1
Neurotic	72.9	73.0	54.9*	62.1	44.7*	67.7
None	17.0	17.6	32.7	24.2	44.7	21.7
Count	*188*	*74*	*113*	*66*	*47*	*378*

*   p < 0.01 compared to the white group.

Table 2.6 considers the CATEGO syndromes rated for respondents who had been positive on the CIS-R (depression) criteria. The similarity between the white and Caribbean profiles is again striking. As in Table 2.5, members of the Pakistani/Bangladeshi group were less likely than those in the white group to have any of the neurotic syndromes and this difference was statistically significant. This was reflected in their greater likelihood to be in the no syndrome group. While members of the Indian/African Asian group were also less like than members of the white group to have an anxiety syndrome, differences here for depression were small and were not statistically significant.

Table 2.6   CATEGO syndromes for those positive on CIS-R (depression) screening

cell percentages

	White	Caribbean	All South Asians	Indian or African Asian	Pakistani or Bangladeshi	All respondents (inc. Chinese)
Psychosis	14.9	9.5	11.5	13.6	8.5	12.7
Depression	79.8	77.0	63.7*	72.7	51.1*	74.6
Anxiety	48.9	39.2	15.9*	13.6*	19.2*	37.0
Other	59.6	54.1	44.3	47.0	40.4	53.7
None	17.0	17.6	31.0	21.2	44.7	21.2
Count	*188*	*74*	*113*	*66*	*47*	*378*

*   p < 0.01 compared to the white group.

Tables 2.5 and 2.6 suggest that the CIS-R operates in a similar way for the white and Caribbean groups. However, the finding in the previous section, that compared with whites and Caribbeans, South Asians who screened positive for psychosis had lower rates of neurosis, is repeated for those in the South Asian groups who screened positive on depression criteria, although here significance tests suggest that the difference might be restricted to the Pakistani/Bangladeshi group.

CONCLUSION

Tables 2.3 to 2.6 show a consistently similar pattern for the white and Caribbean groups. This suggests that the link between the measures used to assess mental health in the initial and the follow-up interviews of Fourth National Survey were equivalent for the two groups. Comparisons between the white and South Asian groups, however, showed a very different pattern. Although the match between the psychosis screening instrument and PSE rates of psychosis were similar for all of the groups, the members of the South Asian groups were far less likely than those in either the white or Caribbean groups to meet the PSE criteria for a neurotic class or syndrome. This was particularly marked for the Pakistani/Bangladeshi group. Although it was also present for the Indian/African Asian group, there was a suggestion in Table 2.6 that this was largely a consequence of a lower rate of anxiety symptoms in the follow-up for this group.

The greater mismatch between CIS-R criteria and the PSE assessment for the South Asian groups compared with others can be explained in two ways. First, as suggested by the CIS-R results presented in Table 2.1, the South Asian groups may simply have had lower rates of neurotic disorders. This is supported by the suggestion in Table 2.1 that they also had lower rates of psychotic disorders, and by the lower rates of psychiatric morbidity among South Asians compared with the general population that have been reported elsewhere (e.g. Cochrane and Bal, 1989). If this was the case, the greater discrepancy between CIS-R and PSE assessments for South Asians could be explained as the CIS-R having a greater false positive rate for South Asians compared with others (in which case the figures for South Asians in Table 2.1 would be an overestimate). This would be consistent with our knowledge that the positive prediction value of a screening instrument decreases as the prevalence of the illness screened for decreases (Bebbington and Nayani, 1995). It is also possible that the time lag between the screening and validation in some way led to more in the South Asian groups than others recovering and forgetting their symptoms. This could be a result of them having less severe or shorter episodes of depression, perhaps as a result of their purported greater access to social support. However, as reported earlier, there is no evidence that the time lag between interviews did influence the reporting of PSE syndromes.

The second possibility is that both the CIS-R and the PSE were not adequate instruments for assessing neurotic disorders among South Asian populations. Such a possibility could explain both the apparently low prevalence of possible depression among the South Asian group according to the CIS-R screening criteria (Table 2.1), and the relatively low proportion of the South Asian groups who were positive on PSE neurosis criteria in both the CIS-R (depression) and PSQ (psychosis) parts of the follow-up validation survey (Tables 2.3 to 2.6). The possibility that both the CIS-R and the PSE assessments of neurosis did not perform well for South Asian groups is not entirely unexpected. As discussed in Chapter 1, when considering the measurement of subjective psychological phenomena it is important to recognise that the meaning of particular words and the concepts that underlie them could have great cultural variation (Kleinman, 1987). This could be a purely technical problem, which could be overcome by making sure that terms describing the appropriate concepts are adequately translated. In fact, for both the initial and follow-up interviews for the Fourth National Survey great care was placed on the translation of interviewer materials. In addition, care was taken to ensure that interviewers at both stages had the appropriate language skills and were ethnically matched, and, in the semi-structured follow-up interview, the interviewer had the flexibility to adjust the wording of questions if he or she deemed this appropriate. This should have meant that the technical translation difficulties involved in an inquiry about psychological phenomena had been minimised.

However, there are also the possibilities that the symptomatic expression of depression was different for those in the South Asian groups compared with members of the white group, or that in attempting to measure depression in this group we were committing what Kleinman (1987) has called a category fallacy (see Chapter 1 for a discussion of this). Indeed, the authors of the PSE appear to accept that it may be reflecting a particular culture when they state that:

> ...the PSE incorporates the views of a school of thought which might reasonably be called Western European in its origins and which is shared by psychiatrists in many other parts of the world (Wing *et al.*, 1974: 11).

If this is the case, then the assessments of depressive disorders among the South Asian groups in this study could be considered to be an underestimate of their true extent of mental disorder. This possibility is tested further in the following chapters.

In contrast, the assessment of possible psychosis in the Fourth National Survey appears to have worked consistently across all ethnic groups, with a similar percentage of those positive on the PSQ screening criteria in each group meeting the PSE criteria for a psychotic diagnosis or syndrome. In terms of the anticipated performance of the PSQ, results are also much as expected. The one in eight of those positive on the PSQ who actually met the criteria for a diagnosis of a non-affective psychosis is consistent with the one in six that the authors of the instrument suggest is likely if it is used in a population with an overall prevalence of 1 per cent (Bebbington and Nayani, 1995). Interestingly, many of those who were positive on the PSQ criteria, but who did not meet the criteria for a psychotic CATEGO class, did meet the criteria for a neurotic CATEGO class.

The overall conclusions of the validation process appear to be that the PSQ (psychosis) indicators worked consistently across all ethnic groups. The CIS-R (depression) indicators worked consistently for the white and Caribbean groups, but did not work in the same way for the South Asian groups and may well have under-estimated their rates of depression. The PSE similarly may have underestimated rates of depression in South Asian groups.

CHAPTER THREE

Estimated Rates of Mental Illness and Use of Medical Services

USING THE VALIDATION FINDINGS TO ESTIMATE RATES OF DEPRESSIVE AND PSYCHOTIC DISORDERS

As described in the previous chapter, most, but not all, of the respondents who scored on the depression and psychosis parts of the initial interview underwent a follow-up clinical interview to assess their mental state more accurately. In the National Psychiatric Morbidity Survey (Meltzer *et al.*, 1995) reasonably accurate assessments of affective disorder were possible by using a standard algorithm to convert CIS-R scores into diagnostic categories. Here the use of a standard algorithm was not possible, because only a part of the CIS-R was asked of respondents. Nevertheless, as shown in Table 3.1, the greater the number of items that the respondents said 'yes' to on the depression and depressive ideas section of the CIS-R the greater the likelihood that they met the criteria for a CATEGO class at the follow-up interview – only a quarter of those who scored on two or three items did not meet any CATEGO criteria and only one in 20 of those who scored on five or more items did not meet any of the criteria, and this relationship was statistically significant ($p < 0.001$, 9 d.f.).

Table 3.1 **Association between CIS-R scores and PSE CATEGO class (only those positive on CIS-R and followed up)**

column percentages

| | CIS-R score on depression and depressive ideas and symptoms lasting more than two weeks | | | |
	One	Two or three	Four	Five or more
CATEGO class				
None	37	26	10	5
Other neurosis/anxiety	37	44	40	23
Neurotic depression	17	26	36	51
Psychosis	9	5	14	21
Base	*46*	*124*	*50*	*99*

More importantly, there was also a clear relationship between the CIS-R score and the likelihood of meeting the criteria for the neurotic depression class. Of those who scored one on the CIS-R, just under one in five met the criteria for neurotic depression compared to one in four for those who scored two or three; one in three for those who scored four; and one in two for those who scored five or more. However, because there was a significant number of respondents who did not meet the CATEGO criteria for neurotic depression despite scoring highly on the CIS-R, individuals could not be considered as cases or not cases on the basis of their CIS-R score alone. Instead the *likely* number of cases of neurotic depression within a particular population was estimated. This was done by using the relationship between the chance of meeting the criteria for neurotic depression and the number of CIS-R items scored – as shown in Table 3.1. That is, if a particular population had five people scoring on one item, five people scoring on two or three items, five people scoring on four items, and five people scoring on five or more items, the estimated weekly prevalence of neurotic depression would be:

$$(5 \times 0.17) + (5 \times 0.26) + (5 \times 0.36) + (5 \times 0.51) = 6.5 \text{ people}$$

This, of course, assumes that the CIS-R and PSE worked uniformly across ethnic groups, which Chapter 2 showed was not the case. If the relationship between CIS-R score and PSE class is considered for ethnic groups separately, the relationship is weaker for the South Asian groups. Despite this, for the estimated rates that are shown in the rest of this report it has been assumed that there was not an ethnic variation in the relationship between CIS-R scores and PSE classes. This has been done on the grounds that there were too few South Asians in the follow-up to produce accurate estimates for them alone and that assuming no variation in confirmation rates by ethnic group would lead to a more conservative assessment of the differences between ethnic groups. Nevertheless it is worth bearing in mind that this has potentially led to an overestimate of the rates of neurotic depression in the South Asian groups – their rates would have been about 20 per cent lower if they were estimated using their lower confirmation rate.

Table 3.2   Association between number of PSQ items scored and PSE CATEGO class (only those positive on psychosis screening and followed up)

column percentages

| | Number of PSQ items scored positive | | |
	One	Two	Three or reports psychotic diagnosis/medication
CATEGO class			
None	31	19	17
Neurotic	57	65	54
Affective psychosis	3	2	8
Non-affective psychosis	9	14	22
Base	*143*	*43*	*65*

In the standard use of the PSQ, respondents are not asked to continue the psychosis screening sequence once they have answered positively to one item. However, in the Fourth National Survey respondents were asked all of the questions regardless of their response to earlier ones. Consequently, a similar approach to that adopted for the CIS-R could be used to identify those with a psychotic disorder. Table 3.2 shows the relationship between the number of items that respondents scored on the PSQ, or responses to questions on a diagnosis of psychosis or taking antipsychotic medication, and the CATEGO class that they were allocated to at follow-up.

This shows a clear relationship between PSQ score and likelihood of meeting a psychotic CATEGO class, and this relationship was statistically significant (for all psychosis $p < 0.005$, 2 d.f., for non-affective psychosis $p < 0.02$, 2 d.f.). Consequently, the likely number of cases of psychotic disorder within a particular population was estimated in the same way as for the CIS-R and neurotic depression. This means that if a particular population had five people scoring on one item, five people scoring on two items, and five people scoring on three or more items or reporting a diagnosis of psychosis or taking psychotic medication, the estimated annual prevalence of non-affective psychosis would be:

$$(5 \times 0.09) + (5 \times 0.14) + (5 \times 0.22) = 2.25 \text{ people}$$

This process is somewhat different from that used in the National Psychiatric Morbidity Survey (Meltzer *et al.*, 1995), where only those who had been validated as a case in the follow-up PSE interview, or who had reported both taking antipsychotic medication and having a psychotic illness, were considered as psychotic. Those who were not successfully followed up and who did not report both a diagnosis of, and treatment for, psychosis were excluded, a conservative approach that would inevitably lead to an underestimate of cases. As the National Psychiatric Morbidity Survey used the standard approach to asking the PSQ, where if the respondent scored on one question subsequent questions were not asked, the kind of estimates of the rates of psychosis made here could not be used. However, it is reassuring to note that if the National Psychiatric Morbidity Survey criteria are used for these data, an almost identical general population rate for non-affective psychosis is recorded. Less reassuring is that the estimate based on the strategy used here is about twice that produced by the more conservative National Psychiatric Morbidity Survey criteria (the details of this are described later).

As for the estimated rate of neurotic depression, this process also assumes that the instruments used to assess psychosis performed uniformly across ethnic group. The tables in Chapter 2 suggest that this was the case, but because of the small number of respondents that were included in the follow-up it is impossible to be sure of this, or to estimate with any accuracy any variation in performance. However, a logistic regression carried out on the follow-up data suggests that the PSQ score was the only variable with a significant effect on predicting the outcome of being assigned a non-affective psychotic CATEGO class.

In addition to the assumptions outlined so far, the estimated rates of both neurotic depression and non-affective psychosis would be subject to sampling error. In this study sampling error would have occurred at both the initial and the follow-up interview, making it extremely difficult to provide an accurate overall assessment of its effect. However, the degree to which sampling error might have affected the validation findings presented in Tables 3.1 and 3.2 is relatively straightforward to calculate, so this will be presented in the relevant tables as 95 per cent confidence limits (i.e. the range of values within which there is a 95 per cent probability that the true value lies), which can be found in brackets underneath the unstandardised and the age and gender standardised overall rates. The small number of respondents followed-up in both the CIS-R and PSQ parts of the sample make this range of values relatively large.

NEUROTIC DISORDERS

Anxiety

As described in Chapter 1, some of the CIS-R questions on anxiety were asked. Although these were not used as selection criteria for the follow-up PSE interview, and consequently could not be validated, responses to these questions are of interest. Here respondents who reported that they were anxious and either had two or more autonomic symptoms (out of: heart racing or pounding; hands sweating or shaking; feeling dizzy; difficulty getting breath; butterflies in stomach; dry mouth; and nausea), or had panic attacks are considered to have anxiety. Table 3.3 shows rates of anxiety by ethnic group, age and gender.

Table 3.3   Anxiety

cell percentages

	White	Irish or other white	Caribbean	Indian or African Asian	Pakistani	Bangladeshi	Chinese
Gender – age standardised							
Male	12	23	11	8	10	2	5
Female	23	32	14	11	11	7	10
Age – unstandardised							
16 to 24	20	*	20	11	5	3	*
25 to 34	21	31	11	9	9	4	*
35 to 54	17	30	12	8	16	8	*
55 plus	12	23	9	10	10	*	*
All ages – unstandardised	16	28	12	9	10	5	8
All ages – age and gender standardised	18	28	13	9	11	5	7
Weighted base	*2664*	*204*	*795*	*1038*	*420*	*137*	*199*
Unweighted base	*2654*	*213*	*614*	*988*	*584*	*289*	*104*

* Cell size too small for a reliable estimate.

Throughout the table there is a gender difference that is consistent with other studies, with women being more likely than men to have reported these symptoms (although differences for the Pakistani group were small). The final row contains age and gender standardised figures to allow for immediate comparisons to be made across ethnic groups. These suggest that the highest rates of anxiety were to be found in the white groups, particularly the Irish or other white group where more than one in four of the respondents reported these symptoms. In fact, the difference between the two white groups was statistically significant. All of the other ethnic groups had lower rates than the white British group, all of these differences were statistically significant, and the difference was particularly large for the Bangladeshi and Chinese groups.

Estimated weekly prevalence of neurotic depression

Table 3.4 shows the estimated weekly prevalence for neurotic depression, an estimate that was based on the correlation between the CIS-R score and the chance of meeting the CATEGO criteria for the neurotic depression class, as shown in Table 3.1. On the whole the gender difference reported elsewhere in the literature was present here, although for some of the groups the differences was small and for the Pakistani group it was reversed. Again, the final age and gender standardised row provides an overall comparison across ethnic groups, and shows that the white minority and Caribbean groups had much greater rates than the white British group (for the Caribbean group this difference was statistically significant). In contrast, the Pakistani group had similar rates to the white group while the Indian/African Asian, Bangladeshi, and Chinese groups all had a lower estimated prevalence of neurotic depression. The prevalence was particularly low for the Bangladeshi and the Chinese groups. It is interesting to note that the differences between the South Asian and white British groups were more marked for women than for men. While women in these groups all had lower rates than white British women, men had similar or, in the case of Pakistani men, higher rates than white British men.

Table 3.4   Estimated weekly prevalence depressive neurosis

cell percentages

	White	Irish or other white	Caribbean	Indian or African Asian	Pakistani	Bangladeshi	Chinese
Gender – age standardised							
Male	2.7	5.8	5.6	2.5	3.8	1.6	1.6
Female	4.8	6.8	6.4	3.2	2.9	2.2	1.7
Age – unstandardised							
16 to 24	3.6	*	6.1	1.3	2.6	0.2	*
25 to 34	3.7	7.5	6.0	3.3	3.5	2.1	*
35 to 54	4.2	5.5	6.7	3.2	4.1	3.7	*
55 plus	3.7	4.0	4.4	3.6	3.1	*	*
All ages – unstandardised[1]	3.8	5.9	5.9	2.8	3.4	1.7	1.6
	(2.6 - 5.1)	(4.2 - 7.7)	(4.0 - 7.8)	(2.0 - 3.7)	(2.3 - 4.4)	(1.2 - 2.3)	(1.0 - 2.1)
All ages – age and gender standardised[1]	3.8	6.3	6.0	2.8	3.4	1.9	1.6
	(2.6 - 5.0)	(4.5 - 8.1)	(4.0 - 7.9)	(2.0 - 3.7)	(2.3 - 4.4)	(1.3 - 2.5)	(1.0 - 2.3)
Weighted base	*2664*	*204*	*795*	*1038*	*420*	*137*	*199*
Unweighted base	*2654*	*213*	*614*	*988*	*584*	*289*	*104*

1 Figures in brackets represent 95 per cent confidence limits that account for sampling error at the follow-up stage of the study.
* Cell size too small for a reliable estimate.

Suicidal thoughts

At the initial interview those respondents who reported depressed mood or loss of interest and scored on any of the first three questions of the depressive ideas section (i.e. felt guilty or blamed him/herself; felt not as good as other people; or felt hopeless) were then asked whether they felt that life was not worth living. This specific question was not validated in the follow-up survey, and was asked of only a highly selected group of respondents (to whom it was most likely to apply), consequently we cannot be entirely certain about interpreting the responses to it, which are shown in Table 3.5.

Table 3.5   Considers life not worth living

cell percentages

	White	Irish or other white	Caribbean	Indian or African Asian	Pakistani	Bangladeshi	Chinese
Gender – age standardised							
Male	1.5	3.1	3.8	1.9	2.8	0.3	0
Female	3.3	4.4	3.8	2.9	3.1	1.3	0
Age – unstandardised							
16 to 24	2.5	*	7.2	1.1	1.6	0	*
25 to 34	1.9	3.3	4.0	2.4	4.0	2.4	*
35 to 54	2.7	4.7	3.3	2.8	4.3	0.4	*
55 plus	2.8	0	2.1	4.3	0	*	*
All ages – unstandardised	2.5	3.2	3.8	2.5	2.9	0.7	0
All ages – age and gender standardised	2.4	3.8	3.8	2.5	2.9	0.9	0
Weighted base	*2664*	*204*	*795*	*1038*	*420*	*137*	*199*
Unweighted base	*2654*	*213*	*614*	*988*	*584*	*289*	*104*

* Cell size too small for a reliable estimate.

Overall this shows a similar pattern to the findings for estimated prevalence of neurotic depression. There was a clear gender difference for the white British group that was less marked for the ethnic minority groups. Both men and women in the white minority and Caribbean groups were more likely than those in the white British group to have reported this symptom (and the difference was just statistically significant for the Caribbean group), although differences were greater for men than for women. Overall rates for the Indian/African Asian and Pakistani groups were similar to those for the white British group, but rates were slightly higher for men and slightly lower for women. And, once again, both men and women in the Bangladeshi group had a rate that was lower than that for all of the other groups (although the difference was not statistically significant) apart from the Chinese, among whom nobody reported this symptom. Interestingly, given the mortality rates for suicide discussed earlier, among South Asians the rates were lowest for the young, and this held regardless of gender (although the comparison here is based on a very small number of respondents).

PSYCHOTIC DISORDERS

Table 3.6 looks at the estimated annual prevalence of non-affective psychotic disorders among the different ethnic groups. Again it is worth emphasising that this was not based on case identification, but on the correlation between the PSQ score and the chance of meeting the CATEGO criteria for a psychotic class, as shown in Table 3.2. The rate for the white British group should be comparable to the general population rate reported in the National Psychiatric Morbidity Survey (Meltzer *et al.*, 1995), but is twice that. If a similar method of case finding to that used in the National Psychiatric Morbidity Survey is used here, the figures become comparable, with a rate of 3.6 per thousand in the white group compared to their general population estimate of 4 per thousand with a standard error of 1 per thousand.[1]

Table 3.6   Estimated annual prevalence of non-affective psychosis rate per 1000

rate per 1000

	White	Irish or other white	Caribbean	Indian or African Asian	Pakistani	Bangladeshi	Chinese
Gender – age standardised							
Male	8	21	10	6	5	5	3
Female	8	7	17	6	6	4	0
Age – unstandardised							
16 to 24	10	*	14	4	5	*	*
25 to 34	7	*	15	7	7	*	*
35 to 54	8	*	13	6	6	*	*
55 plus	6	*	13	9	9	*	*
All ages – unstandardised	8	11	14	6	6	4	1
	(4 - 12)	(5 - 17)	(6 - 21)	(3 - 9)	(3 - 8)	(2 - 6)	(1 - 2)
All ages – age and gender standardised	8	14	13	6	6	4	2
	(4 - 12)	(6 - 21)	(6 - 21)	(3 - 9)	(3 - 8)	(2 - 7)	(1 - 3)
Weighted base[1]	*2663*	*204*	*1567*	*2091*	*862*	*285*	*391*
Unweighted base[1]	*2654*	*213*	*1205*	*2001*	*1185*	*591*	*214*

1 Figures in brackets represent 95 per cent confidence limits that account for sampling error at the follow-up stage of the study.
* Cell size too small for a reliable estimate.

Comparing the age and gender standardised rates (the final row of Table 3.6) shows that both the white minority and the Caribbean groups had rates that were about 75 per cent higher than those of the white British group. The Indian/African Asian and Pakistani groups had rates that were similar to those for the white British group, while the Bangladeshi and the Chinese groups had lower rates. None of these differences were statistically significant. Although the sample size was sufficiently large for statistical tests to detect the three to five times greater rate of psychosis among the Caribbean compared to the white group that would be expected on the basis of previous research, it was not sufficiently large for them to identify

---

1   Differences between the two surveys may also have been a result of the different instruments used. Here the PSE 9 (based on International Classification of Diseases 8 (IDC8)) was used to identify cases, while in the National Psychiatric Morbidity Survey the PSE 10 (based on ICD10) was used.

differences of the size reported here, so the lack of statistical significance should be interpreted with caution.

Interesting gender effects are apparent in Table 3.6,[2] Caribbean women had twice the estimated rate of white British women (a difference that was very nearly statistically significant) and Caribbean men had a rate that was close to that for white British men. The opposite was the case for the white minority group, but this sample was very small making the result unreliable. No clear age effect is present. There was a tendency for the prevalence to decrease with age for the white British group, but not for the Caribbean group, and it possibly increased with age for the Indian/ African Asian and Pakistani groups. Even if smaller age categories are considered for the Caribbean group, there is no evidence that a cohort effect was present in this sample.

If affective psychoses are included in the psychotic category the rates increase slightly for each group. However, because the estimated prevalence was based on a formula that used the probability of an individual with a particular PSQ score being confirmed as positive, rather than true case identification, the pattern across ethnic groups, gender and age for all psychoses is identical to that for non-affective psychotic disorders. Despite this, in order to give some indication of estimated prevalence, it is worth listing the unstandardised estimated prevalence of all psychotic disorders. This was, per 1000 people: 10 for white British; 18 for white minority; 18 for Caribbean; 8 for Indian/African Asian; 7 for Pakistani; 6 for Bangladeshi; and 2 for Chinese.

GP CONSULTATIONS AND TREATMENT

As suggested in the introduction to this report, issues related to ethnic differences in access to and type of treatment are central to the debate on ethnicity and mental illness. Two contrasting possibilities have emerged. In respect to Caribbeans and psychosis there is the possibility that members of this ethnic group, particularly young males, are both more likely to be treated, and more likely to be treated in a coercive manner (e.g. Davies *et al.*, 1996)). For South Asians there is the possibility that differences in observed illness rates are a consequence of under-diagnosis and consequent lower likelihood of treatment. The difficulties with a cross-cultural assessment of mental illness, particularly in a South Asian context, have been explored and discussed in Chapters 1 and 2, and will be returned to in Chapter 4. In addition, the contrast between the evidence presented earlier in this chapter, which suggests that those with Caribbean origins have relatively high rates of depressive neurosis, and evidence reported elsewhere that suggests that they have low treatment rates for depression (Cochrane and Bal, 1989), suggests that under-treatment might also be an issue for the Caribbean population.

---

2   The degree to which any ethnic differences in mental health were consistent for different gender and age groups was routinely examined. This means that a large number of potential interactions between gender and ethnicity, and age and ethnicity, were explored, which, of course, raises the possibility that some of those reported were present in the data purely by chance.

Unfortunately the lack of sufficient information to provide complete diagnoses for all respondents in this study means that these issues can only be explored in a limited way here. (As described earlier, the data collected in this study were primarily based on answers to screening questions, which were then used to *estimate* rates of illness on the basis of findings from a follow-up validation study. At the follow-up interview, from which an accurate diagnosis could be made, only a few respondents were both confirmed as having an illness and were actually receiving treatment, so those data could not be used for an analysis of treatment issues.) Although we can look at consultation rates and treatment rates by response to the screening questions, it is important to remember that a large number of those who screened positive were not actually ill, and some of those who did not screen positive may have been ill. Here two categories of response to the screening questions will be used, both similar to those used for the multivariate analyses that will be presented in Chapters 4 and 5. The first is scoring two or more on the CIS-R (depression) scale, the second is screening positive on the PSQ (but not including the additional psychosis screening items of having a diagnosis of psychosis or taking anti-psychotic medication, both of which would be related to receiving treatment). In order to have sufficiently large sample sizes in each category for this analysis, the following tables show the Pakistani and Bangladeshi group combined.

Table 3.7 looks at consultation rates with a GP for any reason in the last month by CIS-R score, and Table 3.8 does the same for screening positive on the PSQ. For each ethnic group the tables show that those who scored two or more on the CIS-R or screened positive on the PSQ were much more likely than those who did not meet these criteria to have visited their GP in the last month. If only those who had visited their GP three or more times are considered the differences were even greater – those who screened positive on either criteria were more than twice as likely to have visited their GP three or more times.

Table 3.7   Visits to GP in the last month by CIS-R score

			cell percentages: age and gender standardised
	White	Caribbean	Indian or African Asian	Pakistani or Bangladeshi
Score of less than two on the CIS-R				
Visited GP at least once in the past month	32	40	36	51
Visited GP more than twice in the past month	3	7	6	12
Score of two or more on the CIS-R				
Visited GP at least once in the past month	51	58	60	78
Visited GP more than twice in the past month	17	16	15	28
Weighted base	*2859*	*790*	*1021*	*546*
Unweighted base	*2855*	*610*	*966*	*854*

Table 3.8   Visits to GP in the last month by PSQ response

cell percentages: age and gender standardised

	White	Caribbean	Indian or African Asian	Pakistani or Bangladeshi
Not positive on the PSQ				
Visited GP at least once in the past month	32	40	37	51
Visited GP more than twice in the past month	4	7	7	12
Positive on the PSQ				
Visited GP at least once in the past month	43	57	44	54
Visited GP more than twice in the past month	8	15	19	22*
Weighted base	*2860*	*1557*	*2059*	*1127*
Unweighted base	*2855*	*1196*	*1961*	*1739*

* Small cell size makes this figure unreliable.

Comparing the ethnic groups in these tables shows that ethnic minority respondents were more likely to have visited their GP, regardless of their responses to the CIS-R (depression) and PSQ (psychosis). This, of course, needs to interpreted in relation to the general overall higher consultation rates with GPs of ethnic minority people, which is, at least in part, related to their overall greater rates of morbidity (Nazroo, 1997).

Respondents were also asked whether they had consulted their GP in the last year 'about being anxious or depressed or a mental, nervous or emotional problem'. Tables 3.9 and 3.10 show how the responses to this question varied according to the CIS-R and PSQ outcomes. Again a very clear and consistent pattern emerged, for all ethnic groups those who had scored two or more on the CIS-R questions or who had screened positive on the PSQ were at least three times more likely than others to have consulted with their GP about such a problem. Interestingly there was little ethnic variation in such consultations once the CIS-R and PSQ questions had been taken into account.

Table 3.9   Spoken to GP about being anxious, depressed or having a mental, nervous or emotional problem by CIS-R score

cell percentages: age and gender standardised

	White	Caribbean	Indian or African Asian	Pakistani or Bangladeshi
Score of less than two on the CIS-R	8	8	5	6
Score of two or more on the CIS-R	32	29	31	39
Weighted base	*2861*	*790*	*1037*	*545*
Unweighted base	*2858*	*609*	*986*	*873*

Table 3.10   **Spoken to GP about being anxious, depressed or having a mental, nervous or emotional problem by PSQ response**

cell percentages: age and gender standardised

	White	Caribbean	All South Asians
Not positive on the PSQ	9	10	7
Positive on the PSQ	26	31	26*
Weighted base	*2861*	*790*	*1591*
Unweighted base	*2858*	*609*	*1859*

* Small cell size makes this figure unreliable.

Tables 3.11 and 3.12 look at treatment issues. All respondents were asked whether they were currently taking medication and if so what that was. Table 3.11 shows the percentage of respondents who were taking antidepressants or minor tranquillisers by their score on the CIS-R (depression) scale. For the white, Indian/African Asian and Pakistani/Bangladeshi groups there was a clear relationship – those who scored two or more on the CIS-R were more likely to report taking such medication. This relationship did not exist for the Caribbean group, among whom hardly any respondents were taking antidepressants or minor tranquillisers even if they had reported relevant symptoms. It also appears that South Asian respondents who scored two or more on the CIS-R were less likely than equivalent white respondents to be taking such medication, and this difference was particularly large for the Pakistani/Bangladeshi group.

Table 3.11   **Currently treated with anti-depressants or minor tranquillisers by CIS-R score**

cell percentages: age and gender standardised

	White	Caribbean	Indian or African Asian	Pakistani or Bangladeshi
Score of two or more on the CIS-R				
No	1.2	0.2	0.8	0.6
Yes	8.7	0.0	6.4	4.6
Weighted base	*2868*	*796*	*1138*	*555*
Unweighted base	*2867*	*614*	*988*	*873*

Table 3.12 shows the percentage of respondents who were taking antipsychotic medication by whether or not they screened positive on the PSQ (psychosis). Again there seemed to be a clear relationship for all groups except Caribbeans. However, here it appeared that South Asian respondents who screened positive on the PSQ were more likely than their white equivalents to be taking major tranquillisers.

Table 3.12   Currently treated with major tranquillisers by PSQ response

cell percentages: age and gender standardised

	White	Caribbean	Indian or African Asian	Pakistani or Bangladeshi
Positive on the PSQ				
No	0.1	0.7	0.3	0.1
Yes	2.9	0.6	7.1	5.5*
Weighted base	*2868*	*1569*	*2093*	*1146*
Unweighted base	*2867*	*1205*	*2001*	*1776*

* Small cell size makes this figure unreliable.

Respondents were also asked whether they had made use of a variety of other health or social services in the past 12 months. Tables 3.13 and 3.14 focus on responses to the questions on 'therapists', 'social workers or welfare officers' and 'alternative medical practitioners'. (The examples for the latter included Hakim, homeopath and osteopath.) Table 3.13 explores whether the use of these services varied by CIS-R response and ethnic group and shows a consistent pattern for the white and the two South Asian groups. For all three of these groups those who scored two or more on the CIS-R were more likely to have made use of all of these services, although differences appeared to be more marked for the South Asian groups. For the Caribbean group there was little suggestion that the use of these services was related to their responses to the CIS-R questions.

There appeared to be little relationship between screening positive on the PSQ and making use of alternative practitioners (Table 3.14). However, the white and South Asian groups were more likely to have used a therapist if they screened positive on the PSQ, and the white, Caribbean and Pakistani/Bangladeshi groups were more likely to have used a social worker if they screened positive. Interestingly, among those who screened positive on the PSQ a much larger proportion of whites than any other group appeared to have used a social worker.

Table 3.13   Other treatment services used by CIS-R score

Cell percentages: age and gender standardised

	White	Caribbean	Indian or African Asian	Pakistani or Bangladeshi
Therapist				
Scored < 2 on CIS-R	0.7	0.5	0.2	0.2
Scored 2+ on CIS-R	5.4	0.7	6.4	7.6
Social worker				
Scored < 2 on CIS-R	2.6	4.8	1.4	1.3
Scored 2+ on CIS-R	7.0	6.7	8.2	7.2
Alternative practitioner				
Scored < 2 on CIS-R	5.0	3.0	1.9	0.8
Scored 2+ on CIS-R	9.2	1.1	6.1	6.2
Weighted base	*2868*	*796*	*1038*	*555*
Unweighted base	*2867*	*614*	*988*	*873*

Table 3.14   Other treatment services used by PSQ response

cell percentages: age and gender standardised

	White	Caribbean	Indian or African Asian	Pakistani or Bangladeshi
Therapist				
Not positive on PSQ	1.1	0.3	0.2	0.3
Positive on PSQ	2.9	0.0	4.1	4.8*
Social worker				
Not positive on PSQ	2.4	2.1	0.9	0.7
Positive on PSQ	14.4	6.7	1.6	5.0*
Alternative practitioner				
Not positive on PSQ	5.4	1.3	1.1	0.5
Positive on PSQ	6.8	2.1	2.0	2.4*
Weighted base	*2868*	*1569*	*2093*	*1146*
Unweighted base	*2867*	*1205*	*2001*	*1776*

* Small cell size makes this figure unreliable.

Summary

In this chapter ethnic variations in neurotic and psychotic disorders were estimated for the sample from the Fourth National Survey. The estimation was carried out using responses to the CIS-R and PSQ questionnaires, some of which were validated in a follow-up clinical interview using the PSE. Overall a very similar pattern of findings was present for the key outcomes considered: neurotic depression; suicidal thoughts; and non-affective psychosis. Compared to the white British group, for each of these outcomes the white minority and Caribbean groups had higher rates, the Indian/African Asian and Pakistani groups had similar or slightly lower rates, and the Bangladeshi and Chinese groups had considerably lower rates.

However, this pattern was not entirely consistent for men and women. For the three South Asian groups, rates of neurotic disorder were particularly low for women. Indeed, for Indian/African Asian and Pakistani men they were if anything higher than those for the white British group, and for Bangladeshi men the estimated prevalence of neurotic depression was similar to that for the white British group. For the Caribbean and white minority group a similar pattern to that for the South Asian groups was present for neurotic disorders, with the rates for men being much greater and the rates for women being only slightly greater than those for equivalent white British respondents. For psychosis there was also a significant gender variation in relative rates for the Caribbean group, with rates for females being just over twice those of women in the white British group and rates for males being almost the same.

The higher rate of psychosis that was present for the Caribbean group was not as large as might have been expected on the basis of previous work in this area. It was also entirely restricted to women and showed no evidence of a cohort or age effect. The only other ethnic minority group to show a similarly raised rate of psychosis was the white minority group. Also, rates of depression were higher for the Caribbean compared to the white British group, while previous work has suggested that they should be lower. Finally, despite reports of high mortality rates from suicide among young South Asian women, there was no suggestion of higher rates of suicidal thoughts among this group here, although the relationship between suicidal thoughts and actual suicide is by no means straightforward.

However, some caveats need to be added to the interpretation of these findings. First, as shown in Chapter 2, the validation process did not perform uniformly across all groups. Indeed, there was a strong suggestion that the measures of depressive disorder did not perform adequately for the South Asian groups and, as described earlier, this may have led to an *underestimate* of rates. Alternatively, the strategy of ignoring ethnic differences in confirmation rates during the follow-up phase of the study, which was adopted here when estimating rates of depression, may have minimised genuine differences between ethnic groups and led to an *overestimate* of rates of depression for the South Asian groups. The possibilities of under- and over-estimation will be explored more fully in the next chapter, when language and migration effects are considered, but the figures for the South Asian respondents reported in this chapter should be regarded with caution.

Second, there was no validation for some of the outcomes (anxiety and suicidal thoughts), nor for the white minority and Chinese groups, so it remains open to question how well measures performed for these outcomes and these groups. Third, as for depression, the estimated prevalence of psychosis depends on the assumption that the PSQ instrument performed reasonably uniformly across ethnic groups, gender and age (and, for comparisons in later chapters, marital status and socio-economic status). However, as described earlier, as far as it was possible to determine this was the case so this may not have been a serious problem.

The final set of tables in this chapter show a clear relationship between consultations with a GP and responses to the screening questions on depression (CIS-R) and psychosis (PSQ). For all ethnic groups there were higher consultation rates among those who reported symptoms on either of these dimensions of mental illness. However, differences between ethnic groups appeared to emerge when the nature of treatment was considered. Scoring two or more on the CIS-R was also related to a higher rate of taking antidepressants or minor tranquillisers for the white and South Asian groups and screening positive on the PSQ was similarly related to a higher rate of taking major tranquillisers for these groups. However, Caribbeans who met the depression or psychosis screening criteria were no more likely than those who did not to be taking such medication. Indeed, Caribbeans who scored two or more on the CIS-R or who screened positive on the PSQ were much less likely than white or South Asian counterparts to be taking the relevant medication. Also, while the CIS-R score was strongly related to the use of other health services, in addition to GPs, for the white and South Asian groups, the same was not the case for the Caribbean group. For all groups screening positive on the PSQ was related to the use of social workers, but did not appear to be related to the use of therapists or alternative practitioners.

One possible interpretation of these data is that, although Caribbeans who may have had a mental illness were just as likely as other ethnic groups to consult their GP, they were less likely to receive medication or other forms of treatment. It is also possible that if the instruments used underestimated rates of mental illness among the South Asian groups, a larger proportion of those who were ill in these groups than the white group did not receive medication or other forms of treatment.

CHAPTER FOUR

Migration and Fluency in English

INTRODUCTION

The relationship between migration and the prevalence of mental illness among ethnic minority groups is of interest for a number of reasons. First, as discussed in Chapter 1, health status could be related to the chances of migrating. Those with a higher risk of illness may have been more likely to migrate, or it is possible that there might have been a 'healthy migrant' effect for some ethnic minority groups, where those who had a lower risk of illness were selected into the migrant group. Second, it is possible that the social and environmental factors that lead to mental illness might vary among migrant and non-migrant members of ethnic minority groups in Britain. This could be at least part of the explanation for the reported higher rates of psychosis among British-born African Caribbeans (McGovern and Cope, 1987; Harrison *et al.*, 1988). Third, as described in Chapter 1, it has been suggested that research that uses assessments of mental illness based on western psychiatric practice may fail to accurately identify those from non-western cultures who are ill (Kleinman, 1987; Jadhav, 1996). This could be a consequence of translation difficulties, or a consequence of culturally determined differences in the experience and expression of disease. If either of these possibilities were true, detected rates of mental illness among those who were more acculturated should be higher, in which case those born or educated in Britain and those who spoke English fluently would have higher rates of mental illness than those who migrated at an older age or who could not speak English well.

In order to tackle these issues, this chapter will explore whether rates of mental illness among ethnic minority groups varied by migration and, for the South Asian groups, by English language ability. However, a number of technical problems occur when a comparison of this sort is made. First, a decision has to be made between what is and what is not a migrant population. Should respondents who migrated in childhood be regarded as migrants, or, because of their exposure to British schooling and a British childhood environment, should they be considered as non-migrants? If we agree with the later decision, at what age should the cut-off between migrants and non-migrants be made? For the purposes of the comparisons made here, a distinction has been drawn between those who were born in Britain or who migrated below the age of 11 (called 'non-migrants' in this volume) and those who migrated aged 11 or older (called 'migrants' in this volume). This is somewhat arbitrary and chosen to provide as balanced a sample as possible. However, perhaps because of the small number of respondents affected by such a decision, the results presented are similar to those that are produced if the cut-off is made at the age of five or based on country of birth.

The second and perhaps most obvious problem is that the ages of migrant and non-migrant members of the Fourth National Survey's ethnic minority sample are very different, with little overlap in age groups. For example: the mean age of Caribbeans born in Britain was 26 (standard deviation = 6) while that of Caribbeans born elsewhere was 50 (standard deviation = 13); the mean age of Indians and African Asians born in Britain was 22 (standard deviation = 5) while that of Indians and African Asians born elsewhere was 43 (standard deviation = 14); and the mean age of Pakistanis and Bangladeshis born in Britain was 21 (standard deviation = 4) while that of Pakistanis and Bangladeshis born elsewhere was 39 (standard deviation = 14). This means that only respondents within specific age bands can be used to make the comparison between migrants and non-migrants and even within these fairly narrow age bands the data need to be age and gender standardised. Unfortunately, small sample sizes mean that for the process of standardisation the Pakistani and Bangladeshi groups have had to be combined, and the Chinese group has been dropped.

Third, because of differences in when different ethnic groups migrated to Britain, the age bands that are focused on vary from ethnic group to ethnic group. For Caribbeans the age group is 30 to 44, for Indians and African Asians it is 25 to 39 and for Pakistanis and Bangladeshis it is 20 to 34.

NEUROTIC DISORDERS

Anxiety

Table 4.1 considers whether age on migration was related to whether respondents reported that they felt anxious and had either two or more associated autonomic symptoms or panic attacks. For all three ethnic minority groups non-migrants reported much higher rates than migrants, and this difference was statistically significant for the Indian/African Asian group. The final row of the table shows the rate for white respondents in the same age group as the ethnic minority respondents. As in Table 3.3 in the previous chapter, this rate remained higher than that for all of the ethnic minority groups regardless of age on migration.

Table 4.2 shows a similar effect for English language ability. Those South Asian respondents who were fluent in English reported higher rates of anxiety than those who were not, but not rates that were as high as the equivalent white group. However, the differences between the fluent and not fluent groups were not statistically significant.

Table 4.1   Anxiety by age on migration to Britain

cell percentages: age and gender standardised

	Caribbean	Indian or African Asian[1]	Pakistani or Bangladeshi
Age on migration to Britain			
11 or older	7	5	5
British born or < 11	16	12	9
Equivalent white rate	20	21	21
Weighted base	*242*	*385*	*222*
Unweighted base	*221*	*393*	*349*

1 p < 0.01

Table 4.2   Anxiety by fluency in English – South Asians only

cell percentages: age and gender standardised

	Indian or African Asian	Pakistani or Bangladeshi
Fluency in English		
Not fluent	6	5
Fluent	8	10
Equivalent white rate	21	21
Weighted base	*378*	*213*
Unweighted base	*382*	*340*

Estimated weekly prevalence of neurotic depression

Table 4.3 looks at the relationship between age on migration and the estimated rate of neurotic depression (which is estimated using the formula described in the previous chapter). The table shows a similar effect for the two South Asian groups – migrants had much lower rates of depression than non-migrants. This difference was close to statistical significance for the Indian/African Asian group. For the Caribbean group differences were small, but both migrants and non-migrants reported higher rates than the equivalent white group, as shown for the total Caribbean group in Table 3.4 in the previous chapter. In contrast to this, for the two South Asian groups the lower than white rate shown in the previous chapter was only present for those who had migrated to Britain when they were aged 11 or older. Non-migrants in the Pakistani/Bangladeshi group had the same rate as the equivalent white group, while those in the Indian/African Asian group had a slightly higher rate than the equivalent white group.

Table 4.4 explores the relationship between fluency in English and the estimated prevalence of neurotic depression. As for anxiety, those South Asians who were fluent in English reported higher rates than those who were not, although the differences were not statistically significant. Again it is interesting to note that the rate for those who were fluent in English was similar to that for the equivalent white group.

Table 4.3   Estimated weekly prevalence of neurotic depression by age on migration to Britain

cell percentages: age and gender standardised

	Caribbean	Indian or African Asian[1]	Pakistani or Bangladeshi
Age on migration to Britain			
11 or older	6.9	1.8	1.6
British born or < 11	7.9	5.2	3.7
Equivalent white rate	4.3	3.8	3.8
Weighted base	*242*	*385*	*221*
Unweighted base	*221*	*393*	*349*

1 p = 0.05

Table 4.4   Estimated weekly prevalence of neurotic depression by fluency in English – South Asians only

cell percentages: age and gender standardised

	Indian or African Asian	Pakistani or Bangladeshi
Fluency in English		
Not fluent	2.0	1.9
Fluent	3.6	3.9
Equivalent white rate	3.8	3.8
Weighted base	*377*	*214*
Unweighted base	*382*	*340*

Suicidal thoughts

As described previously, at the initial interview those respondents whose previous responses to the CIS-R questions indicated that they might have depression were asked whether they had considered that life was not worth living. Although the differences shown in Table 4.5 were only statistically significant for the Pakistani/ Bangladeshi group, they show a striking effect. Less than 1 per cent of ethnic minority respondents who had migrated to Britain aged 11 or older met this criterion. Rates for non-migrant ethnic minority respondents were between three and a half and more than seven times higher than those for their migrant counterparts, and also higher than for equivalent whites. Given the debate around the higher rates of mortality from suicide among young South Asian women, it is interesting to note that there was no great gender variation in this symptom for the non-migrant South Asian group (both men and women had a rate of 3.8 per cent), and rates for non-migrant female South Asian respondents were similar to those for equivalent female white respondents (who had a rate of 3.3 per cent) – all of the ethnic difference shown was a result of higher rates among non-migrant South Asian men.

Table 4.6 shows a smaller, but similar, effect for fluency in English. Once again the difference was only statistically significant for the Pakistani/Bangladeshi group.

Table 4.5   Considers life not worth living by age on migration to Britain

cell percentages: age and gender standardised

	Caribbean	Indian or African Asian[1]	Pakistani or Bangladeshi
Age on migration to Britain			
11 or older	0.7	0.9	0.6
British born or < 11	4.9	3.3	4.4
Equivalent white rate	3.1	2.3	2.1
Weighted base	*242*	*385*	*222*
Unweighted base	*221*	*393*	*349*

1   p < 0.05

Table 4.6   Considers life not worth living by fluency in English –
             South Asians only

cell percentages: age and gender standardised

	Indian or African Asian	Pakistani or Bangladeshi[1]
Fluency in English		
Not fluent	1.2	1.1
Fluent	2.2	4.7
Equivalent white rate	2.3	2.1
Weighted base	*378*	*213*
Unweighted base	*382*	*340*

1   p < 0.05

PSYCHOTIC DISORDERS

Table 4.7 shows the estimated annual prevalence of non-affective psychosis among migrant and non-migrant ethnic minority groups, calculated using the formula described in Chapter 3. Unlike the findings for some of the neurotic disorders, the Caribbean group showed no difference according to age on migration to Britain, with both Caribbean groups having rates about twice that for the equivalent white group. However the two South Asian groups showed a similar pattern to the findings for neurotic disorders, with non-migrants having rates that were twice those of migrants and similar to those for the equivalent white group. The differences between the migrant and non-migrant Indian/African Asian and Pakistani/Bangladeshi groups were statistically significant.

Table 4.8, which shows the relationship between the estimated prevalence of non-affective psychosis and fluency in English for the two South Asian groups, also has a similar pattern to those for neurotic disorders. Respondents who were fluent in English reported higher rates than those who were not, and for the Pakistani/ Bangladeshi group the rate was twice as high and the difference was statistically significant.

Table 4.7 **Estimated annual prevalence of non-affective psychosis by age on migration to Britain**

rate per 1000: age and gender standardised

	Caribbean	Indian or African Asian[1]	Pakistani or Bangladeshi[2]
Age on migration to Britain			
11 or older	14	4	3
British born or < 11	13	8	8
Equivalent white rate	7	8	8
Weighted base	*486*	*763*	*453*
Unweighted base	*427*	*803*	*695*

1 p < 0.01
2 p < 0.005

Table 4.8 **Estimated annual prevalence of non-affective psychosis by fluency in English – South Asians only**

rate per 1000: age and gender standardised

	Indian or African Asian[1]	Pakistani or Bangladeshi[2]
Fluency in English		
Not fluent	4	4
Fluent	6	8
Equivalent white rate	8	8
Weighted base	*751*	*427*
Unweighted base	*787*	*668*

1 p = 0.08
2 p < 0.05

The small estimated number of cases of psychosis among the groups considered in Tables 4.7 and 4.8 means that the findings need very careful interpretation. However, if a cruder, but more common, indicator of possible psychosis – being positive on one of the PSQ questions or having a diagnosis of psychosis or taking antipsychotic medication – is considered, a very similar pattern is present. These findings are shown in Tables 4.9 and 4.10.

Table 4.9 **Positive on psychosis screening by age on migration to Britain**

cell percentages: age and gender standardised

	Caribbean	Indian or African Asian[1]	Pakistani or Bangladeshi[2]
Age on migration to Britain			
11 or older	9.7	2.9	1.9
British born or < 11	10.2	6.9	6.1
Equivalent white rate	5.3	5.6	6.3
Weighted base	*486*	*763*	*453*
Unweighted base	*427*	*803*	*695*

1 p < 0.01
2 p < 0.005

Table 4.10 **Positive on psychosis screening by fluency in English –
South Asians only**

cell percentages: age and gender standardised

Fluency in English	Indian or African Asian[1]	Pakistani or Bangladeshi[2]
Not fluent	2.8	2.8
Fluent	5.5	6.2
Equivalent white rate	5.6	6.3
Weighted base	*751*	*427*
Unweighted base	*787*	*668*

1 p = 0.08
2 p < 0.05

UNPACKING MIGRATION AND LANGUAGE EFFECTS

Throughout the previous tables in this chapter, fluency in English and age on migration to Britain had similar effects for the two South Asian groups. As these two factors were highly related (very few respondents born or educated in Britain were not fluent in English) this is not surprising. However, in terms of interpreting the findings for the South Asian groups they are conceptually very different. If the difference was a result of fluency in English and not age on migration to Britain, the issue could be simply one of inadequate translation. If the difference was one of country of birth and education rather than fluency in English, there would be a stronger case for suggesting that the pattern of findings were a consequence of the problems highlighted by Kleinman (1987) of undertaking cross-cultural psychiatric research. (Of course other explanatory factors are related to age on migration and fluency in English, and these may account for the differences shown. This issue, and the consequence need for multivariate analysis, will be discussed in the next chapter.)

Table 4.11 explores the inter-relationships between age on migration, fluency in English and mental health for South Asians – who have had to be combined into one group because of the small sample size once several factors are considered together. The two right hand columns consider those who were migrants and show that for this group fluency in English appeared to make no difference and, if anything, was related to a lower rate of mental illness for most of the outcomes. However, the two left hand columns suggest that there was a relationship between fluency in English and mental illness for those who were non-migrants, with those who were fluent having higher rates for all of the outcomes. A slightly more consistent pattern is suggested by the table for the effect of migration. Comparing the first and third columns shows that among those who were fluent in English migrants had a much lower rate of mental illness according to all of the outcomes considered. And comparing the second and fourth columns shows a similar, although less clear, pattern for those who were not fluent in English.

Table 4.11   Mental illness, age on migration and fluency in English for South Asians

cell percentages unless otherwise stated: age and gender standardised

	British born or migrated aged under 11		Migrated to UK aged 11 or older	
	Fluent in English		Fluent in English	
	Yes	No	Yes	No
Anxiety	12	4	3	5
Neurotic depression	5	2	1	2
Considers life not worth living	4	3	1	1
Weighted base	*219*	*56*	*132*	*184*
Unweighted base	*245*	*64*	*142*	*271*
Rate of non-affective psychosis (per 1000)	9	7	3	4
Positive on psychosis screening	6.8	5.9	3.6	2.0
Weighted base	*490*	*90*	*245*	*354*
Unweighted base	*523*	*105*	*276*	*551*

Interestingly, the table on the whole shows the same pattern of findings for all of the outcomes considered, including psychosis, suggesting that the effect under consideration was not one that was specific to depression, or even neurotic disorders more generally.

An alternative way to try and unpack the relative contribution of language and migration effects to the differences shown in earlier tables is to carry out a logistic regression. Here two logistic regression models were tested, each with the main effects of age on migration and fluency in English and the interaction between these as independent variables, but with a different outcome: scoring two or more on the CIS-R; and either being positive on the PSQ or having a diagnosis of psychosis or taking antipsychotic medication.[1] The findings are presented in Table 4.12, which strongly suggests that the biggest effect was related to age on migration. Fluency in English by itself had little impact on the outcomes (an odds ratio of 1.0 for a variable indicates that it makes no difference to the outcome), although the interaction between fluency and age on migration (i.e. being both fluent and being a non-migrant) did have some effect for the CIS-R (depression) outcome. A backward elimination procedure, where the significance of the relationship between dependent and independent variables is used to eliminate from the model those variables that do not make an important contribution, was also carried out. The result of this only included age on migration in the models for being positive on psychosis screening. For the CIS-R outcome migration and the interaction term made similar contributions, as suggested by the full model odds ratios. Overall, then, this suggested that the issue was not one of inadequate translation of the interview materials.

---

1   Logistic regression depends on having a dichotomous outcome variable (i.e. ill or not ill) rather than one with many categories, which means that the full range of CIS-R or PSQ scores could not be used here, either as outcomes in themselves or to estimate actual rates of depressive or psychotic disorder.

Table 4.12 **Logistic regression: age on migration, fluency in English and the interaction between these two for all South Asians[1]**

Variable	Score of two or more on CIS-R Odds ratio	Positive on psychosis screening Odds ratio
Born in UK or migrated < 11	2.3	3.2
Fluent in English	1.0	1.5
Interaction term	1.9	0.6

1 Age and gender were entered as control variables, but only those of approximately the same age are used to avoid gross age effects (the model remains much the same if all ages are included).

SUMMARY

For the Indian/African Asian and the Pakistani/Bangladeshi groups there was a consistent pattern throughout this chapter. Migrants reported lower rates of mental illness than non-migrants regardless of the outcome considered. A similar, although not so strong, pattern emerged when fluency in English was considered, with those who were not fluent having lower rates of mental illness than those who were. However, when age on migration and fluency in English were considered at the same time, it appeared that the main effect was related to the age on migration variable. In fact, given the extent to which we attempted to overcome translation problems, with the matching of interviewers and the careful translation of materials, this is perhaps not too surprising. Interestingly, when making a comparison to the rate of mental illness reported by the white group, the tables also showed that the lower rates for South Asians reported in the previous chapter were not present for those who were fluent in English, or who were born in Britain or migrated under the age of 11.

The interpretation of these finding is not straightforward. They may reflect a genuine difference in mental health between the migrant and non-migrant South Asian populations. This would not be entirely unexpected – elsewhere data from this survey have been used to show that the physical health of migrants is on the whole better than that of non-migrants, although the differences were nowhere near as big as those reported here (Nazroo, 1997). Others have suggested that the health of migrant populations begins to approximate that of the host population within one or two generations (Syme *et al.*, 1975; Gordon, 1982). Also, differences shown here for Caribbeans followed a similar pattern to those for the two South Asian groups for the anxiety and suicidal thoughts outcomes, although they did not for depression or psychosis. If the findings were a consequence of genuine differences in the health of migrants and non-migrants two key explanations might be relevant. First, differences could be a consequence of a healthy migrant effect, where the most healthy are selected into the migrant group, an effect that would disappear with subsequent generations. Second, the differences could be a consequence of the negative impact of the British environment on the mental health of ethnic minority people, particularly those who had spent at least part of their early childhood in Britain. Such an effect could be a consequence of cumulative differences in the actual level of disadvantage experienced – a possibility supported by evidence suggesting that the length of time spent in Britain was directly related to poorer physical health among the South Asian population of Glasgow (Williams, 1993) – or of differences in the interpretation of and response to the disadvantage experienced.

Of course we should consider the possibility that the findings presented in this chapter were not a reflection of genuine differences between migrant and non-migrant groups, but a consequence of a measurement artefact related to Kleinman's (1987) category fallacy. The great care that was taken over the translation of materials into different languages and the language matching of interviewers, and the evidence presented in the later tables of this chapter, suggest that translation as such was not an issue here. Nevertheless, when a debriefing of the interviewers used for the follow-up PSE based study was held, one of the themes raised by the South Asian interviewers from all of the communities in question was the difficulty of translating the term 'depression' into South Asian languages. Many of the interviewers said that there was no direct equivalent for depression in the relevant languages, that the terms used in the translated interviewer material were unfamiliar to them and that interviews in a language other than English took considerably longer than those in English. This clearly raises the possibility that even translated assessments undertaken by ethnically matched interviewers would not be completely effective and that the concept itself did not translate.

Evidence to support this proposition comes from the tables that showed that age on migration to Britain was strongly related to the possibility of being identified as mentally ill and that, in addition, age on migration appeared to be more related to this risk than fluency in English. The finding that within the non-migrant group English language ability was related to risk of being identified as mentally ill, while within the migrant group this was not the case, also lends strong support to the possibility that the issue is one of cultural distance rather than a direct consequence of the process of migration as discussed above. Those South Asians who were born or educated in Britain and were fluent in English would be those who would be expected to be most acculturated. In contrast, it would be expected that both migrant South Asians, and non-migrant South Asians who were not fluent in English, would still have a significant cultural distance from western psychiatry. Overall, the evidence certainly lends strong support to the possibility that the instruments used were, to a certain extent at least, culturally-bound and failed to assess adequately the extent of mental illness among the South Asian populations covered by the survey.

Finally it is worth considering the findings on psychotic disorders for the Caribbean group. The previous chapter suggested that the rates of psychosis among Caribbeans were higher than those for the general population, but not as high as other, treatment based, research has suggested. It also suggested that these higher rates did not exist for Caribbean men, only being present for Caribbean women, and that there was no evidence for an age or cohort effect among this group. This chapter has suggested that the higher rates among second generation African Caribbeans reported elsewhere did not appear in this nationally representative community sample. Here Caribbeans born in Britain or who migrated below the age of 11 had almost identical rates of psychosis to those who migrated aged 11 or older, and if the age on migration cut-off was reduced to five years, or to only those born in Britain, the pattern of findings was identical.

CHAPTER FIVE

Exploring Mental Health Variations Further

INTRODUCTION

So far this volume has outlined the extent to which the data collected demonstrated ethnic variations in mental health, and how these may have been influenced by straightforward demographic factors such as age and gender. However, as was pointed out in the introduction, a number of other factors are related to mental health and these may influence the extent of variation across ethnic groups. The degree to which this may occur is explored here, initially with an analysis of the effects of marital status and social class. Then multivariate models will be presented to show the extent of variation in mental health, once certain key factors have been considered, both *within* and *across* different ethnic groups.

MARITAL STATUS

Among the general population the National Psychiatric Morbidity Survey (Meltzer *et al.*, 1995) showed a strong relationship between marital status and mental illness. For both men and women the lowest rates of neurotic and psychotic disorders were found among the married, while women who were lone parents had very high rates of both neurotic and psychotic disorders. The following tables explore the rate of mental illness by marital status in this study. To ensure confidence in the findings presented, there has to be sufficient respondents in each ethnic/gender/marital status category. Consequently, the small white minority and Chinese groups could not be included in this analysis, and the South Asian groups have had to be combined into one. For the men there is a straightforward comparison between those who were married or cohabiting and those who were single. For the women a third category has been included, lone parents with children under the age of 11. There were very few South Asian respondents who were lone parents, so findings for that group should be treated with some caution. When considering these tables it is important to remember that there is a relationship between marital status and age, and that these data have not been standardised to deal with this. Consequently some of the effects shown here may be confounded by the small age effects shown in Chapter 3.

Neurotic disorders

Table 5.1 shows the percentage of people who reported feeling anxious and having either two autonomic symptoms or panic attacks, while Table 5.2 does the same for the estimated weekly prevalence of neurotic depression (as determined using the formula shown in Chapter 3).

Table 5.1   Anxiety by gender and marital status

			cell percentages
	White	Caribbean	All South Asians
Men			
Married or cohabiting	11	9	8
Single	14	12	8
Women			
Married or cohabiting	19	15	9
Single	23	10	12
Lone parent with children under 11	39	18	28*
Weighted base	*2867*	*783*	*1596*
Unweighted base	*2867*	*614*	*1861*

*   Unweighted cell count is only 29 cases.

Table 5.2   Estimated weekly prevalence of neurotic depression by gender and marital status

			cell percentages
	White	Caribbean	All South Asians
Men			
Married or cohabiting	2.9	6.2	2.8
Single	3.6	4.5	2.3
Women			
Married or cohabiting	3.8	7.6	2.9
Single	5.6	4.0	2.5
Lone parent with children under 11	11.2	7.4	14.4*
Weighted base	*2867*	*783*	*1596*
Unweighted base	*2867*	*614*	*1861*

*   Unweighted cell count is only 29 cases.

Both tables show a very similar pattern. Among the men there was no clear relationship between neurotic disorder and marital status, although there was a suggestion that single white and Caribbean men might have had higher rates of anxiety than their married or cohabiting counterparts and that the opposite was the case for depression among Caribbean men. It is interesting to note that the differences between the men in different ethnic groups for neurotic disorders, as shown in Chapter 3, remained regardless of marital status.

Among the women there was also a consistent relationship across the two tables, but this varied across ethnic groups.[1] For the white group there was a very clear relationship, lone parents had the highest rate of illness, followed by single women and then married or cohabiting women, who had the lowest rate. This is consistent with the findings reported in the National Psychiatric Morbidity Survey (Meltzer *et al.*, 1995). The South Asian group showed a similar pattern, although the difference between single and married or cohabiting women was not great. The estimated weekly prevalence of neurotic depression was more than one in ten for both white and South Asian lone parents. For Caribbean women, rather surprisingly, those who were single reported the lowest rates of neurotic disorder, and they also reported lower rates than their white counterparts. Differences between Caribbean women who were lone parents and married or cohabiting were not great, lone parents reported slightly higher rates for anxiety, while for depression they were more or less equal.

Bearing in mind the differences between the women in different ethnic groups that were shown in Chapter 3, taking marital status into account made very little difference to the pattern of findings for anxiety. However, the higher estimated prevalence of neurotic depression reported there for Caribbean compared with white women only existed here for those who were married or cohabiting. Caribbean women who were single or lone parents had a lower estimated prevalence of neurotic depression than their white counterparts. In contrast, the overall lower estimated prevalence of neurotic depression that was shown for South Asian women in Chapter 3 remained for single and married or cohabiting women, but not for lone parents who had more or less the same estimated prevalence as the equivalent white group.

Table 5.3   Considers life not worth living by gender and marital status

cell percentages

	White	Caribbean	All South Asians
Men			
Married or cohabiting	1.0	2.3	2.3
Single	3.1	5.7	1.4
Women			
Married or cohabiting	1.5	3.6	2.4
Single	4.4	1.3	2.8
Lone parent with children under 11	8.3	7.6	14.6*
Weighted base	*2867*	*783*	*1596*
Unweighted base	*2867*	*614*	*1861*

*   Unweighted cell count is only 29 cases.

Table 5.3 shows those respondents who reported that they sometimes considered that life was not worth living. The relationship between this and marital status was very much as expected for white and Caribbean men, those who were single were

---

1   The extent to which the differences by marital status was consistent across ethnic groups was routinely examined. This means that a large number of potential interactions between gender, marital status and ethnicity were explored, raising the possibility that some of those reported were present in the data purely by chance.

much more likely to report this symptom. However, the opposite was the case for South Asian men.

For white and South Asian women the relationship was again as might be expected and followed that for anxiety and depression. Lone parents had the highest rates (one in 12 white lone parents reported this symptom) and married or cohabiting women had the lowest rates. However, among the Caribbean women those who were single had the lowest rates, although, unlike for the other outcomes so far considered, here lone parents were more likely to have reported that they considered life not worth living than their married or cohabiting counterparts.

Psychotic disorders

Using the formula outlined in Chapter 3, Table 5.4 shows the estimated annual prevalence of non-affective psychosis by marital status. Among white men those who were single had the highest estimated prevalence, but for men in both of the ethnic minority groups non-affective psychosis was not related to marital status. Overall the differences reported in Chapter 3 between the men from different ethnic groups remained the same regardless of marital status, although it is interesting to note that single Caribbean men had a slightly lower estimated prevalence than their white equivalents.

Table 5.4   Estimated annual prevalence of non-affective psychosis by gender and marital status

	White	Caribbean	rate per 1000 All South Asians
Men			
Married or cohabiting	7	10	6
Single	11	10	6
Women			
Married or cohabiting	6	16	4
Single	9	17	9
Lone parent with children under 11	14	20	12
Weighted base	*2867*	*1567*	*3238*
Unweighted base	*2867*	*1205*	*3777*

Women from all three of the ethnic groups showed a similar pattern. Lone parents had the highest estimated prevalence, followed by those who were single, with those who were married or cohabiting having the lowest estimated prevalence, although the differences were less marked for the Caribbean group. It is worth noting that the pattern for Caribbean women here does not follow that for the other outcomes covered in this chapter, and that taking account of marital status made no difference to their overall higher estimated prevalence compared with the other ethnic groups.

Of course the estimated annual prevalence of non-affective psychosis is low (less than 1 per cent for most groups) and this makes the findings for the small sample sizes in Table 5.4 fairly unreliable. Table 5.5 uses the more common, but less accurate, indicator of being positive on one or more of the psychosis screening criteria (i.e. saying yes to a PSQ question or reporting a diagnosis of psychosis or taking antipsychotic medication). Reassuringly the pattern for this was almost identical to that for the estimated annual prevalence.

Table 5.5   Positive on psychosis screening by gender and marital status

cell percentages

	White	Caribbean	All South Asians
Men			
Married or cohabiting	5.9	7.1	4.1
Single	8.1	9.2	4.6
Women			
Married or cohabiting	4.1	12.5	2.8
Single	6.5	14.1	6.0
Lone parent with children under 11	9.2	21.2	10.8
Weighted base	*2867*	*1567*	*3238*
Unweighted base	*2867*	*1205*	*3777*

Summary

Overall for the male respondents there was no relationship between mental illness and marital status (as crudely measured here). The only possible relationships were higher rates of suicidal thoughts for single white and Caribbean men and higher rates of psychotic disorders for single white men. For white and South Asian women there was a consistent pattern: lone parents reported the highest rate of mental illness and married or cohabiting women reported the lowest rates. For Caribbean women this pattern was only present for psychotic disorders. For neurotic disorders and suicidal thoughts single Caribbean women had the lowest rate and there was not much difference between lone parents and married or cohabiting women.

It is worth noting that rates of lone parenthood vary across ethnic groups. In this survey, 4.3 per cent of white women and 3.3 per cent of South Asian women were lone parents with a child younger than 11, while this was the case for one-fifth of Caribbean women. (Note that when making a comparison of rates of lone parenthood the younger age profile of women in ethnic minority groups need to be considered. For a full interpretation of this see Modood *et al.* (1997).) However, differences between ethnic groups largely remained consistent regardless of marital status. The main exception to this was for Caribbean women and depression. In contrast to the overall higher estimated prevalence of neurotic depression among Caribbean women compared with white women, single Caribbean women and Caribbean women who were lone parents had a lower estimated prevalence than equivalent white women.

SOCIAL CLASS

Table 1.1 shows that three common indicators of socio-economic position varied greatly across the different ethnic groups included in this study. Broadly speaking white, Indian/African Asian and Chinese groups were in comparable positions, and Caribbean, Pakistani and Bangladeshi groups were worse off. And, as mentioned in Chapter 1, others have pointed out that because socio-economic factors vary across ethnic groups they need to be considered when comparisons of rates of illness are made. However, a number of problems arise when attempting to take into account socio-economic factors for the purpose of making such comparisons. These have been discussed in detail, and in the context of this survey, elsewhere (Nazroo, 1997), but here two are worth briefly restating.

First, the indicators of socio-economic status typically used in health research can mean very different things for different ethnic groups. For example, within a particular tenure group, such as owner-occupier, the quality of housing and the level of overcrowding varies dramatically across ethnic groups, with owner-occupiers in some ethnic groups having housing that is much poorer than other groups and equivalent to that of those who are renting (Modood *et al.*, 1997). Similarly, within a particular class group the equivalised household income (i.e. total household income adjusted for the number of people living within the household) varies by ethnic group, with ethnic minority groups within a particular class tending to have a lower income than that of equivalent white people (Nazroo, 1997). Finally, among the unemployed ethnic minority people tend to have been out of work for considerably longer than white people (Modood *et al.*, 1997). All of this means that we cannot say that people from a particular class/tenure/employment group are on average equivalent across ethnic groups. This makes the process of standardising for socio-economic status across ethnic groups very difficult.

Second, and relatedly, it may be misleading to even attempt to standardise for socio-economic factors when making comparisons across ethnic groups. The central problem here is that once controls have been applied the influence of such factors on health within ethnic (minority) groups becomes obscured and their explanatory role lost. Consequently, the following figures will concentrate on showing how social class might be related to mental health *within* particular ethnic groups. It is also worth reiterating that the presentation of data that has been standardised for class obscures the points made in the previous paragraph, and leaves the reader (and researcher) to assume that all the necessary 'controls' have been applied and that the differences that remain are a 'pure' ethnic or race effect. Nevertheless, as argued elsewhere (Nazroo, 1997), there is some merit in this process if it is carried out and interpreted cautiously, so later logistic regression models will be presented to show the effect of applying controls to ethnic differences.

In order to make the comparisons across socio-economic groups in this chapter, a simple distinction has been made between three categories, which are based on a combination of Registrar General's class and employment status. Class was assigned using the head of the household's occupation. Where it was not clear which household member was the head of the household (e.g. where there was more than one working adult), class was allocated on the basis of gender (with men's occupations being used in preference to women's) and generation (e.g. a father's occupation being used in preference to a son's if the father was below retirement age). A simple distinction here was made between households that were manual and non-manual.

Finally, a third group of respondents from households containing no full-time worker was identified.

Once again the data presented have been age and gender standardised to allow for a straightforward comparison to be made across class and ethnic groups. However, because of the small sample sizes in particular age and gender cells, this meant that the Pakistani and Bangladeshi group have had to be combined, and that the white minority and Chinese groups could not be considered. Those aged 65 or older have also had to be dropped from this analysis.

Neurotic disorders

Figure 5.1 shows the relationship between anxiety and class, while Figure 5.2 does the same for the estimated weekly prevalence of neurotic depression.

For three of the ethnic groups, Caribbeans, Indian/African Asians and whites, the figures show that there was a reasonably clear relationship. Overall those in non-manual households had the best health according to these indicators and those in households with no full-time worker had the worst health, although there was no difference between the manual and non-manual categories for the Caribbean group and depression. For the Pakistani/Bangladeshi group there did not appear to be any clear relationship between class and the risk of having a neurotic disorder.

Figure 5.3 shows the variation by social class for the rate of respondents reporting that they sometimes felt that life was not worth living. Once again there was a very clear and inverse relationship between this symptom and social class for the Caribbean, Indian/African Asian and white groups. For the Pakistani/Bangladeshi group there did not appear to be a straightforward relationship, although those from households with no full-time worker had the highest rates.

Figure 5.1   Anxiety by class

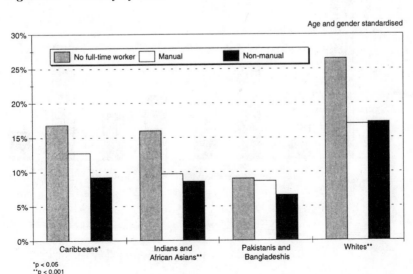

$^*p < 0.05$
$^{**}p < 0.001$

Figure 5.2   Estimated weekly prevalence of neurotic depression by class

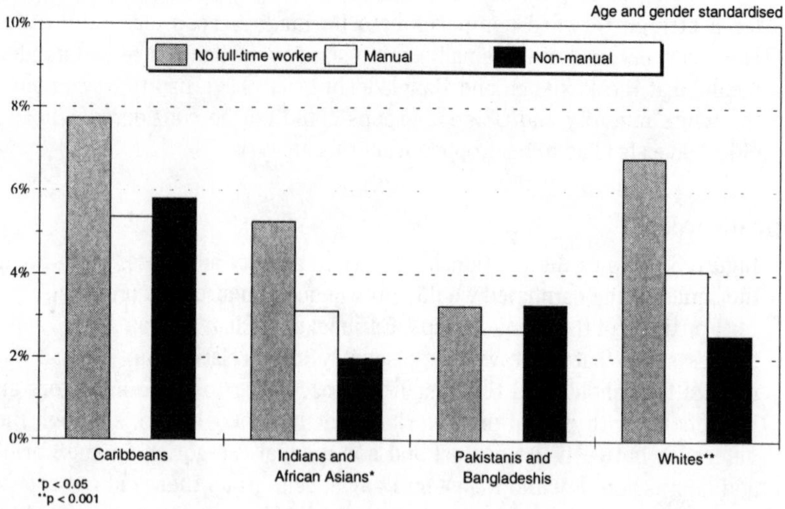

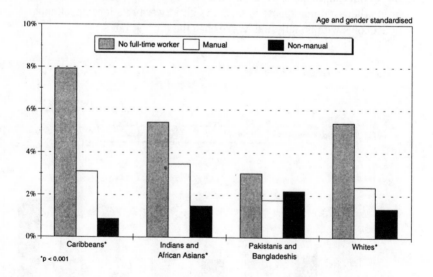

Figure 5.3   Considers life not worth living by class

Figure 5.4   Estimated annual prevalence of non-affective psychosis by class

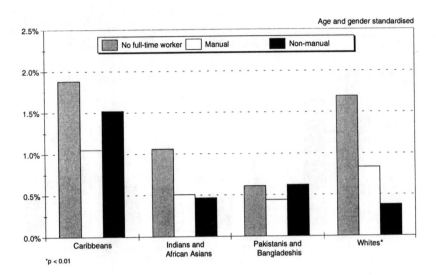

Psychotic disorders

The estimated annual prevalence of non-affective psychotic disorders was determined using the formula described in Chapter 3. Figure 5.4 shows the relationship between this and social class by ethnic group. Again it is worth pointing out that the small number of estimated cases makes the interpretation of this figure uncertain. Figure 5.5 provides some confirmatory evidence by showing how the less specific, but more common, rate of screening positive on any of the psychosis items (the PSQ, reporting a diagnosis of psychosis, or taking antipsychotic medication) varied by social class.

For the white group both figures show that there was a strong inverse relationship with class. A similar, but not so strong, pattern was present for the Indian/African Asian group, while, once again, there was no clear relationship for the Pakistani/Bangladeshi group. For the Caribbean group, as expected, those from households with no full-time worker had the highest rates of psychosis – the estimated annual prevalence of non-affective psychosis was almost 2 per cent for this group. However, unexpectedly, those in manual households appeared to have lower rates than those from non-manual households. Here it is also interesting to note that Figure 5.4 suggests that most of the difference between the Caribbean and white groups can be accounted for by the relatively high rate among non-manual Caribbeans. Rates for Caribbeans from households with no full-time worker and those that were manual were only slightly higher than those for equivalent white respondents, while the difference for those from non-manual households was four-fold.

Figure 5.5 Positive on psychosis screening by class

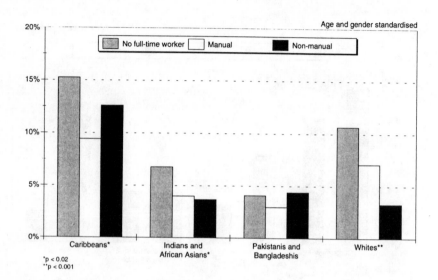

Summary

Throughout these figures showing the relationship between social class and mental health there was a clear and inverse relationship for the white and Indian/African Asian groups. In contrast, the Pakistani/Bangladeshi group did not appear to show any relationship between class and mental illness. The Caribbean group showed the expected inverse relationship between class and mental health for neurotic disorders, although for them there was no difference between the manual and non-manual categories for depression. In addition, the pattern for this group was not so clear for psychotic disorders. Although those from households with no full-time worker had the expected higher rate, those from non-manual households had higher rates than those from manual households.

Of course, as discussed earlier, the interpretation of these figures is by no means straightforward. Throughout this volume a number of factors beyond ethnicity have been shown to be related to the risk of reporting mental illness, including gender, marital status, age on migration and social class. In addition, the causal direction and causal mechanisms linking these factors and risk of mental illness are by no means clear or open to easy interpretation in a cross-sectional survey such as this. Nevertheless, multivariate analysis can be used to begin to unpack the relative importance of individual factors and how they contribute to both within and across ethnic group differences. The results of this are presented below.

MULTIVARIATE ANALYSIS

There are two central reasons for carrying out multivariate analyses on these data. First, as just described, the tables and figures so far presented in this and the two previous chapters have shown that a number of factors might contribute to poorer mental health. However these factors are highly inter-related and without multivariate analysis it becomes impossible to separate out their relative effects and to explore whether these effects vary greatly according to specific outcomes. Second, given that some of the factors so far covered are likely to make a significant impact on the risk of mental health, and that they also vary by ethnic group, it would be worthwhile to see how ethnic variations in mental health differ as contributory factors are controlled for – although, as discussed above, it should be recognised that the degree of 'control' that is possible is limited by the sensitivity of the measurement of potential contributory factors.

The multivariate analyses carried out here were done using logistic regression. Two outcomes have been considered: scoring two or more on the depression and depressive ideas section of the CIS-R; and screening positive on a psychosis item (the PSQ, reporting a diagnosis of psychosis, or taking anti-psychotic medication).[2] Because of the need to have sufficiently large samples only three ethnic groups have been considered here: a white group; a Caribbean group; and a South Asian group. The South Asian group contains Indians, African Asians, Pakistanis and Bangladeshis, even though earlier tables show that there were some differences between these groups. Areas where such differences might be relevant to the multivariate analyses presented here will be discussed as the findings are presented.

The data in the subsequent tables are laid out in terms of odds ratios for specific effects. These reflect the relative chance of an individual with a particular characteristic meeting the mental illness criteria being considered, compared to an individual with the reference characteristics (which are described at the foot of each table). Odds ratios greater than 1.0 indicate a greater chance, while those lower than 1.0 indicate a smaller chance. The further the odds ratio is from 1.0 (either higher or lower) the greater the effect. In addition to the size of an effect we also need to consider the possibility that an effect has been found in these data as a result of chance. This has been done by identifying in the tables odds ratios that are statistically significant.

Differences within ethnic groups

Table 5.6 shows the odds ratios from three separate logistic regression models (one for each main ethnic group) predicting the outcome of scoring two or more on the CIS-R depression and depressive ideas sections.

The model for the white group is very much as would be expected from previous studies and earlier tables. Those who were female, lone parents, poorer and middle-

---

2   As discussed in Chapter 4, logistic regression depends on having a dichotomous outcome variable (i.e. ill or not ill) rather than one with many categories, which means that the full range of CIS-R or PSQ scores could not be used here, either as outcomes in themselves or to estimate actual rates of depressive or psychotic disorder.

aged had the highest rates. The young and old had similar rates and those who were single had higher rates than those who were married or cohabiting.

The Caribbean group's model showed a similar set of effects for class, gender and age – although those who were young also had higher rates. However the pattern was very different for marital status, both those who were single and those who were lone parents had much lower rates than those who were married or cohabiting. Finally, Caribbeans who were born in Britain or who migrated at an early age had slightly higher rates than those who migrated aged 11 or over.

Table 5.6   **Logistic regression model for CIS-R score of two or more on depression and depressive ideas section**

	White	Caribbean	*odds ratios* All South Asians
Age			
16 – 24	1.1	1.6	0.2**
25 – 34	1.7*	1.6	0.7
35 – 54	1.9**	1.5	1.1
Gender			
Female	1.2	1.3	0.9
Marital status			
Single no children aged < 11	1.5*	0.5*	1.4
Lone parent	2.5**	0.4*	3.7**
Class			
Manual	1.7**	1.1	1.5
No full-time worker	2.5**	1.8*	2.0*
Age on migration			
Born in Britain or migrated < 11	n/a	1.2	2.2**

*   p < 0.05
** p < 0.01

Odds ratios are compared to: age 55 plus, male, married/cohabiting, non-manual and, for Caribbeans and South Asians, migrated to Britain aged 11 or over.

Again the model for the South Asian group had some similarities with and differences from that for the white group. There was a similar effect for class and marital status, with those who were poorer and who were lone parents having the highest rates (although, as suggested by Figure 5.2, separate models for Indian/African Asians and Pakistani/Bangladeshis indicated that the class effect was greater for the former). However, gender was not related to risk beyond lone parenthood and those who were aged under 35 had much lower rates than those who were older. A very strong effect for age on migration was present in the model for the South Asian group, with non-migrants having an odds ratio that was greater than two.

The three models presented in Table 5.7 consider the chance of screening positive on psychosis (i.e. being positive on the PSQ, reporting a diagnosis of psychosis, or taking antipsychotic medication).

Table 5.7   Logistic regression model for screening positive on psychosis

odds ratios

	White	Caribbean	All South Asians
Age			
16 – 24	2.1*	1.5	0.3**
25 – 34	1.8*	1.3	1.0
35 – 54	2.4**	1.0	0.9
Gender			
Female	0.7a.s.	1.9**	0.8
Marital status			
Single no children	1.4	1.2	2.1**
Lone parent	1.5	1.1	2.4a.s.
Class			
Manual	2.4**	0.9	1.0
No full-time worker	3.4**	1.4	1.3
Age on migration			
Born in the UK or migrated < 11	n/a	0.8	1.8*

a.s. $p < 0.07$
* $p < 0.05$
** $p < 0.01$

Odds ratios are compared to: age 55 plus, male, married/cohabiting, non-manual and, for Caribbeans and South Asians, migrated to the UK aged 11 or over.

The model for the white group shows the expected effects, younger, poorer, males were more likely to screen positive, although lone parents also had a greater risk (very few lone parents worked, so it was impossible to use the class indicator to assess the possible contribution of poverty to this).

The model for the Caribbean group suggested that the major contribution to risk was gender, women were twice as likely as men to have screened positive. Other effects for the Caribbean group were small, but younger respondents were more likely to screen positive. There did not seem to be a clear class effect for the Caribbean group. As shown in the straightforward cross-tabulation, non-manual workers had a slightly greater risk than manual workers, although those from households with no full-time worker had the highest rate. Also as shown in earlier cross-tabulations, non-migrant Caribbeans seemed to have had a lower risk than their migrant counterparts.

The model for the South Asian group again showed that lone parents had a greater risk of screening positive for psychosis, despite the slightly lower risk for women overall. In contrast to the models for the other ethnic groups, the data for South Asians suggested that younger people had a lower risk, although those who were single had a much higher risk. Like the other models, there was a suggestion that those in households with no full-time worker had a greater risk than others, although, as for the CIS-R, separate models for Indian/African Asians and Pakistani/ Bangladeshis suggested that the class effect was much greater for the former group. Most striking is the contribution made by migration to the findings, as for depression non-migrant South Asians had a much greater risk than migrants.

Differences across ethnic groups

Four models comparing Caribbeans and South Asians with whites for two outcomes – scoring two or more on the depression and depressive ideas section of the CIS-R, and screening positive on psychosis – are detailed below. Some additional caution needs to be used in the interpretation of these models. Because the relative sizes of the ethnic minority populations in the models are much greater than those found in the general population, the size and significance of effects shown cannot be generalised to the population of Britain. This type of generalisation can only be done with very careful consideration of the models presented in previous section, which show effects for particular ethnic groups. However, the models shown here are useful in helping to understand the relative contribution of various factors to producing the differences found between the ethnic groups in this sample.

The models here have been laid out as a series of points. These show how the odds ratios for ethnic group differences alter as other factors related to variations in mental health are progressively added to the models. Model 1 compares the white with Caribbean groups for scoring two or more on the CIS-R.

Model 1   Whites and Caribbeans compared for scoring two or more on the depression and depressive ideas sections of the CIS-R

1   Model with age and gender gives Caribbeans an odds ratio of 1.8, $p < 0.01$.

2   With class added Caribbeans have an odds ratio of 1.6, $p < 0.01$.

3   With marital status and age on migration added the odds ratio for Caribbeans remains unchanged.

4   With an interaction between being Caribbean and marital status added Caribbeans in general have an odds ratio of 1.3, p is not significant.

  (a) A model for single respondents (regardless of whether they have children) with age and gender included gives single Caribbeans compared to single whites an odds ratio of 0.9, p is not significant.

  (b) A model for respondents who were married or cohabiting, with age and gender included, gives Caribbeans an odds ratio of 2.5, $p < 0.01$.

    (i) With indicators of standard of living and employment added to the model for married and cohabiting respondents the odds ratio for Caribbeans becomes 2.1, $p < 0.01$.

    (ii) Differences between married and cohabiting Caribbeans and whites were only present for those Caribbeans who were born in Britain or migrated younger than 11. (The sample size is too small to test this further.)

The implication of Model 1 is that most (if not all) of the higher rate of scoring two or more on the CIS-R for Caribbeans was a result of the higher rate among those who were married or cohabiting compared to their white counterparts. The addition of factors related to socio-economic and migration status progressively reduced the odds ratio for Caribbeans, suggesting that such factors made an important contribution to the differences that were present.

Model 2 looks at the CIS-R score for the South Asian compared with the white group. The implication of this model is very clear. All of the difference between the white and the South Asian groups can be attributed to a factor related to migration status. South Asians born in Britain or who migrated at an early age had the same risk as the white group, while those who migrated aged 11 or older had a much lower risk.

Model 2   Whites and South Asians compared for scoring two or more on the depression and depressive ideas sections of the CIS-R

1   Model with age and gender gives South Asians an odds ratio of 0.7, $p < 0.01$.

2   With marital status and class added the odds ratio for South Asians remains unchanged.

3   With age on migration added South Asians have an odds ratio of 0.9, p is not significant.

Models 3 and 4 look at screening positive on a psychosis item, the first comparing the Caribbean and white groups.

Model 3   Whites and Caribbeans compared on screening positive for psychosis

1   Model with age and gender gives Caribbeans an odds ratio of 2.3, $p < 0.01$.

2   With class added Caribbeans have an odds ratio of 2.1, $p < 0.01$.

3   With marital status and age on migration added Caribbeans have an odds ratio of 1.9, $p < 0.01$.

4   With an interaction between Caribbean and gender added Caribbeans in general have an odds ratio of 0.5, p is not significant, while female Caribbeans have an odds ratio of 2.4, $p < 0.01$.

   (a) A model only for men and including age gives Caribbeans an odds ratio of 1.2, p is not significant.

   (b) A model only for women and including age gives Caribbeans an odds ratio of 3.2, $p < 0.01$.

      (i) With indicators of marital status, age on migration, standard of living and employment added to the model for women, Caribbean women have an odds ratio of 2.3, $p < 0.01$.

Model 3 suggests that all of the difference between the Caribbean and the white groups could be attributed to the much higher rate for Caribbean compared with white women. There was no difference between Caribbean and white men. Once other socio-economic and demographic factors were added into the model for Caribbean women their odds ratio compared with white women dropped by a third (although the difference from 1.0 was still statistically significant), suggesting that such factors made an important contribution to the difference.

Model 4   Whites and South Asians compared on screening positive for psychosis

1   Model with age and gender gives whites an odds ratio of 0.7, $p < 0.01$.

2   With marital status and class added the odds ratio for whites remains unchanged, but $p < 0.03$.

3   With age on migration added whites have an odds ratio of 0.9, p is not significant.

Once again Model 4 suggests that age on migration was the crucial variable explaining the difference between the white and South Asian groups. Non-migrant South Asians had very similar rates to the white group, while those who migrated to Britain aged 11 or over had much lower rates.

SUMMARY

The models presented in this section require careful interpretation. There are two central problems. First, the models simply provide some indication of an association between factors, or how risk varies across groups and sub-groups. There is no way of determining causal direction in a study such as this. Second, there are concerns about how appropriate the variables used are for making comparisons within and across ethnic groups. Earlier it was suggested that they have problems in this respect, and a more detailed description of these problems can be found in Nazroo (1997). Nevertheless some provisional conclusions can be drawn.

It is apparent that *within* ethnic groups there was considerable variation in mental health and this was related to the socio-economic and demographic factors considered. Although gender, age, marital status and age on migration were all related to the outcomes considered in the models exploring variations *within* ethnic groups, their effects were not consistent across ethnic group, nor across type of outcome. The most consistent effect was that for class. Throughout these models social class seemed to be inversely related to mental health for all of the outcomes considered and for all of the ethnic group except, possibly, Pakistani/Bangladeshis. For the other groups, those from households with no full-time worker had particularly poor mental health.

For the models comparing ethnic minority groups with the white group, differences were largely restricted to sub-groups within the ethnic minority group.

For the South Asian group, the overall lower rate for both outcomes could be attributed to the much lower rate for those who migrated to Britain aged 11 or over. Those who were younger on migration or were born in Britain had the same rate as the white group, and this effect held regardless of age, gender, social class, or, as shown in Chapter 4, fluency in English. The suggestion may be that the instruments used were not entirely adequate for assessing mental health for the South Asian groups.

For the comparison between the white and Caribbean groups, differences were largely related to marital status and gender. The higher rate for Caribbeans of scoring two or more on the depression and depressive ideas sections of the CIS-R was due to the higher rate among Caribbeans who were married or cohabiting. Caribbeans who were single or who were lone parents had the same rate of scoring two or more on the CIS-R as equivalent whites. The higher rate of screening positive for psychosis among Caribbeans was entirely due to the higher rate among women, Caribbean men had the same rate as white men. It is also interesting to note that as far as could be tested these differences between ethnic sub-groups and the white group were at least partly accounted for by socio-economic and other demographic factors.

CHAPTER SIX

Conclusion

INTRODUCTION

The context of this study and report were described in some detail in the introduction. However, it is worth going over the key points here and outlining the strengths and weaknesses of this study before the central findings are discussed.

Previous research on ethnic variations in mental health has largely focused on psychotic illnesses. This has repeatedly shown that African Caribbeans are at least three times more likely than whites to be admitted to hospital with a first diagnosis of schizophrenia (Bagley, 1971; McGovern and Cope, 1987; Harrison *et al.*, 1988; Littlewood and Lipsedge, 1988; Cochrane and Bal, 1989; King *et al.*, 1994; Van Os *et al.*, 1996). Although this work has been less clear about the relative rates of psychosis among South Asian groups, they seem to have about the same or slightly higher rates than those found for the general population (Cochrane and Bal, 1989; King *et al.*, 1994).

Data on hospital and general practice treatment have also been able to give indications of the relative rates of depression in different ethnic groups (Cochrane and Bal, 1989; Gilliam *et al.*, 1989). These have suggested that rates of depression are, if anything, lower in South Asian groups than in the general population. Similarly, but in contrast to their high treatment rates for psychosis, this work has also shown that African Caribbeans have low rates of depression.

However, these studies have to be regarded with some caution. Almost all of them have been based on treatment statistics, and they are often based only on data on hospital admissions. Such data contain a number of difficulties that limit our ability to generalise from them (and which were discussed in detail in the introduction). Most important here is that differences in the pathways into care for different ethnic groups, rather than differences in rates of illness, may have influenced the pattern of findings reported. The concern is that African Caribbeans with a psychosis may be more likely than equivalent whites to end up in hospital, and, in contrast, that South Asians with a mental illness may be less likely to do so. One possible reason for differences in pathways into care is that they are a consequence of cultural differences in the expression and experience of mental illness. On the one hand this might lead to under-treatment among some ethnic groups, a concern that applies particularly to South Asians and depression. On the other hand, it is possible that cultural differences between ethnic minority people and white psychiatry and research could lead to the over-diagnosis and overestimation of mental illness in some groups, particularly as far as African Caribbeans and psychosis are concerned. Consequently, there remains some doubt about the quality and interpretation of the data based on treatment statistics that have been published to date (Kleinman, 1987; Sashidaran, 1993).

There must be less doubt about another aspect of research on ethnic variations in mental illness – suicide rates. Mortality data have shown that those born in the Caribbean and most of those born in South Asia have low rates of suicide compared to the general population, but young women born in India and East Africa have much higher rates (Soni Raleigh, 1996). However, the fact that mortality data can only be analysed by country of birth, which, especially for the young, is a poor indicator of ethnic background, limits the scope of these data. The interpretation – that the higher rates are a consequence of culture conflict (Merril and Owens, 1986; Biswas, 1990; Handy *et al.*, 1991; Soni Raleigh and Balarajan 1992) – is also controversial. It is possible that the identified 'culture' conflict is not much different from what would be called 'family' conflict for a young white woman (Lipsedge, 1993; Karmi *et al.*, 1994).

As the above has implied, one of the central problems with our current understanding of the relationship between ethnicity and mental illness is that it has been limited by the shortcomings of available data. The Fourth National Survey presented a unique opportunity to overcome some of these shortcomings. This study comprised a large nationally representative survey of the main ethnic minority groups in Britain, together with a comparison survey of the white population. The survey was community based, so not dependent on the prior identification of potentially ill people. It also contained a large enough sample in the white, Caribbean and South Asian groups to allow the pattern of findings based on treatment statistics to be tested. Unfortunately only a small Chinese sample was included in the study, so only a limited amount could be said about this group. Similarly, the study was not designed to cover white minority groups, so, although some were included in the sample, again only a little could be said about them. Another significant advantage of the survey was that it covered a range of other topics concerning the lives and experiences of the respondents, which consequently meant that it offered an opportunity to explore the important question of whether the various forms of social disadvantage faced by ethnic minority people contributed to their risk of mental illness (Sashidharan, 1993).

The Fourth National Survey's initial assessment of mental illness was limited by time constraints and the by skills of lay interviewers, who were trained in social rather than psychiatric research. This meant that the initial structured interview on its own could not be as accurate in case identification as a clinical study. Methodological developments made during the National Psychiatric Morbidity Survey (Meltzer *et al.*, 1995) – including the use of the CIS-R, the development of the PSQ, and the linking of a structured survey with a clinical follow-up study – were a great help here. The mental health assessment in the Fourth National Survey followed a similar design to that used in the National Psychiatric Morbidity Survey (the differences between the two studies are outlined at the end of Chapter 1). Respondents who appeared to be possibly suffering from a depressive or psychotic disorder, on the basis of their responses to the depression and depressive ideas sections of the CIS-R and their responses to the PSQ, were re-contacted and underwent a clinical interview based on the PSE. This enabled the relationship between responses to the CIS-R and PSQ questions in the initial interview to be compared to the PSE-derived diagnostic class that applied to the respondents who were followed-up. The results of this comparison then allowed the CIS-R and PSQ responses to be used to estimated the prevalence of neurotic depression and non-affective psychosis in each group. (See the introduction to Chapter 3 for a more detailed discussion of the rationale for this and the procedure adopted.)

Clearly there are some problems with such a strategy for estimating the prevalence of mental illness. The most important of these is that it depends on the assumption that the three instruments used to assess mental illness worked uniformly across different groups, such as respondents and non-respondents to the follow-up, men and women, different classes, and different ethnic groups. Although the evidence suggests that on the whole they did perform consistently, there is a possibility that this was not the case for the South Asian groups compared to the other ethnic groups. The similarity in the performance of the screening and validation instruments for the white and Caribbean groups was striking, and allows us to be reasonably confident when making comparisons between them. However, as will be discussed later, there was a suggestion that both instruments failed to identify some of those in the South Asian groups who were mentally ill.

KEY FINDINGS

Throughout the body of the report findings have generally been ordered according to the outcome under consideration, such as depression or psychosis. Here the discussion will be ordered slightly differently, being divided into four sections: findings for the Caribbean group; findings for the South Asian group; findings for the white minority and Chinese groups; and social factors contributing to mental illness.

Estimated rates of mental illness for the Caribbean group

Although the annual prevalence of non-affective psychosis estimated here was higher for the Caribbean group compared to the white group, the difference was not as great as the three to five times higher rate that treatment statistics have suggested. The overall rate was less than twice as high and this difference was not statistically significant (Table 3.6). In addition, all of the difference was a result of the higher rate among Caribbean women compared to white women. Rates for Caribbean men were the same as those for white men. Other work has suggested that hospital admissions for first onset schizophrenia are particularly high among Caribbean men born in Britain and among young Caribbean men (e.g. Harrison *et al.*, 1988). There was no evidence here to support either of these propositions. Table 4.7 shows that there was no difference between migrant and non-migrant members of the Caribbean group in the estimated annual prevalence of psychosis. In addition, the estimated prevalence of psychosis for Caribbean men did not vary greatly by age, and differences compared with the white group were at their smallest for the young

(Table 3.6). The lack of an age or cohort effect among this group also suggests that the greater risk that has been reported for them elsewhere was not a consequence of the exposure of a particular cohort to an environmental hazard (Glover, 1989).

So there was no evidence in this sample to suggest that Caribbean men had higher rates of psychosis than white men. Caribbean women, however, did appear to have rates that were twice as high as white women, although this difference also did not quite reach the criteria for statistical significance. Multivariate analyses presented in Chapter 5 confirmed this pattern, and also suggested that socio-demographic factors, such as class and marital status, might have contributed to the possible differences in the prevalence of psychosis between white and Caribbean women (Model 3).

Although these data do suggest that the rates of psychosis are not elevated in the Caribbean population to anything like the extent suggested by treatment statistics, there are a number of reasons why this interpretation might be mistaken. First, it is possible that the difference between the findings presented here and treatment statistics are a consequence of differences in the ways in which the number of ill people is counted. Treatment statistics are based on *incidence* rates, counting each new case of psychosis within a specific time period. The rates presented here were based on the *prevalence* of cases of psychosis within a particular population and time period. Although this difference might at first sight seem trivial, if the time between onset and recovery from illness is different for compared populations, the different methods of counting would produce different findings. This is simply because the prevalence count would be relatively lower in the population that was recovering more quickly as fewer of the onsets would still be ill in the time period that was covered. Consequently, if Caribbeans with psychosis were likely to have a shorter illness than their white counterparts, the prevalence rates presented here would have under-estimated differences in incidence. There is some evidence to support this possibility, both McGovern *et al.* (1994) and McKenzie *et al.* (1995) showed that Caribbeans with psychosis had a better prognosis than whites. But, such differences would have to be fairly large to account for the relatively large differences in prevalence rates during a one year period presented here and incidence rates presented elsewhere.

Second, it is possible that the community survey that this study was based on was more likely to have failed to include those who had a psychosis in the Caribbean group than the white group. That is, the lower rate of psychosis among Caribbeans in this study might have been a consequence of an under-coverage of that group. The survey did not include institutions such as prisons and psychiatric hospitals, where young Caribbean men are more likely than any other group to be found, and such men may be more likely to suffer from a psychotic disorder (NACRO, 1995). And, as far as can be determined, refusal to participate in the study was highest among young Caribbean men (see Chapter 1). However, to explain the findings presented here such an effect would have to be specific to young Caribbean men with a psychotic disorder and to not be present for others with a psychotic disorder. No assessment was made at the point of attempted recruitment into the study, so it is impossible to determine whether this was the case, but because young men in the other ethnic minority groups also had higher refusal rates, the refusal rate for young Caribbean men was not surprisingly high.

Another possibility is that the exclusion of one element of the PSQ for screening purposes – whether the respondent thought that people were plotting to cause him/her harm – lead to an underestimate of psychosis in the Caribbean group. The rationale for this exclusion was presented in Chapter 1. However, although Caribbeans were almost twice as likely to report this symptom than whites at the initial interview, the size of this difference was no greater than that for the other items of the PSQ (Table 2.1). This means that this item of the PSQ did not perform a more important role for Caribbeans than for the other ethnic groups and, consequently, its omission was not likely to have lead to a greater underestimate in rates of psychosis for them.

Overall then, it seems that while we should take these problems seriously, they were unlikely to have lead to an underestimate in the rates of psychosis *specifically* for the Caribbean group. The parallel between the findings presented here and those for the Epidemiological Catchment Area (ECA) survey in the United States also lends support to the conclusions reached. Although treatment rates for psychosis among Black Americans are much higher than those for their white counterparts, the ECA survey showed that once age, gender, socio-economic position and marital status had been taken into account there were no differences between blacks and whites in the prevalence of psychosis (Adebimpe, 1994).

Findings for the estimated weekly prevalence of neurotic depression among the Caribbean group also contradicted findings based on treatment statistics. Table 3.4 showed that the Caribbean group had a 60 per cent higher rate of depression than the white group and that this difference was statistically significant. While the difference was present for both men and women, it was greater for men, with Caribbean men having twice the rate of white men. Interestingly, much of the difference between the white and Caribbean groups here was related to marital status. Caribbean men and women who were single or lone parents had the same or lower rates of depression compared to their white counterparts, while those who were married or cohabiting had twice the rate of their white counterparts.

Estimated rates of mental illness for the South Asian group

The apparent difference between the South Asian and white groups in the performance of the instruments used here to assess mental illness makes comparisons between these groups and assessments of actual rates of illness for South Asians more difficult. Evidence for the difference in their performance comes from a variety of findings in this study.

First, when making comparisons between the instruments used for the initial interview and the PSE used in the follow-up interview, the rate of confirmation of neurotic illness was much lower for the South Asian groups and this difference was statistically significant. It is possible that this reflected a genuine difference in rates of depression, but the fact that the confirmation rate for psychosis was identical for the white and South Asian groups and that the lower confirmation rate for neurosis occurred in both the depression and the psychosis halves of the follow-up study, makes it possible that this was a consequence of a difference across ethnic groups in the performance of the mental health assessments used.

Second, findings presented in Chapter 4 suggest that the estimated prevalence of mental illness among the South Asian groups was much higher for those who were born in Britain or had migrated to Britain at an early age, compared with those who had migrated to Britain aged 11 or older. The estimated prevalence was also higher for those South Asians who were fluent in English. However, when age on migration and fluency in English were considered at the same time the suggestion was that the former was most important. A more detailed exploration of Table 4.11 highlights an additional point. If age on migration and fluency in English could be considered as surrogate indicators for acculturation, those who were the most acculturated (i.e. those who were both non-migrants and fluent in English) had the highest rates for all of the indicators of mental illness considered. This is the pattern of findings that we would expect to find if there was a problem with the cross-cultural use of these instruments.

Finally, a debriefing of interviewers used for the follow-up PSE based interview also suggested that the instruments did not perform quite as well as they could have. Interviewers reported difficulties with the translations they were given, that they themselves had difficulty translating concepts appropriately into South Asian languages and that interviews with those who were not fluent in English took much longer than those with respondents who were fluent. This bears some similarity to the findings reported by researchers who have explored the cross-cultural relevance of western psychiatry and found important differences from the western pattern in the expression of mental illness in South Asian groups (Krause, 1989; Fenton amd Sadiq-Sangster, 1996).

Overall, this provides support for Kleinman's (1987) critique of cross-cultural research and suggests that the instruments used failed to assess accurately the prevalence of mental illness among the South Asian groups. If this were the case, our best estimates would come from the rates identified for the non-migrant groups, which Models 2 and 4 in Chapter 5 suggest are identical to those for the white group for both depression and psychosis.

On the other hand, if we believe that this evidence about the relative performance of the screening and validation instruments is not convincing and accept that the differences between the white and South Asian groups estimated here are genuine, the overall pattern that emerges is one of a relatively healthy South Asian population. All of the South Asian groups had lower rates of anxiety and depression, although the differences were greater for migrants than for non-migrants and for women than for men. Indeed, for depression there was little difference between white and Indian/African Asian men and, if anything, Pakistani men had higher rates than white men. A similar pattern to that for neurotic disorders was present for psychotic disorders. The Indian/African Asian and Pakistani groups had a slightly lower estimated annual prevalence of non-affective psychosis than the white group, while the rate for the Bangladeshi group was much lower.

This comparison between the South Asian and white groups and the comparison between the individual South Asian groups produces some puzzling findings. One would expect the economically better off Indian/African Asian group to have the lowest rates of mental illness, while the worst off Bangladeshi group should have the highest. (See Table 1.1 for an indication of the socio-economic positions of the different ethnic groups.) The fact that the opposite was the case requires some investigation. One explanation might lie in the nature of the social support available to members of these groups. For example, it is possible that the location of Bangladeshis in particular geographical areas gives them greater access to support networks, which help them to cope with the various forms of social disadvantage that they face in those locations (see Halpern (1993) for a discussion of these issues), although in a small local study MacCarthy and Craissati (1989) found no evidence to support this position.[1]

As described earlier, there has been considerable concern about the high mortality rates from suicide among young women born in South Asia (Soni Raleigh, 1996). Here respondents who had key symptoms of depression on the CIS-R were asked if they felt that life was not worth living at the initial interview. Responses to this question suggested that the Indian/African Asian and Pakistani groups had similar rates of suicidal thoughts to the white group, while the Bangladeshi group had a lower rate. And this finding was present across gender and age groups. Consequently, this evidence was not consistent with the pattern of findings for mortality rates from suicide. This discrepancy between the rates of suicidal thoughts among young South Asian women reported here and the mortality rates among young women born in South Asia reported elsewhere, suggests an interesting line of enquiry into how the pathways that lead from suicidal thoughts to actual suicide might differ across ethnic, gender and age groups. However, the assessment of suicidal thoughts made here was very crude, so it may not have been a good indicator of the levels of distress that would lead to an actual suicide attempt, let alone one that results in death. So, the findings on suicidal thoughts reported here should be interpreted with a great deal of caution.

Estimated rates of mental illness for the white minority and Chinese groups

Both the white minority and Chinese groups had small sample sizes, so only a limited analysis could be carried out for them. In addition, the instruments used to assess the prevalence of mental illness could not be validated for these groups. This might be particularly important for the interpretation of the findings for the Chinese group whose culture, on the whole, could be considered to be significantly distanced from western psychiatry. Indeed, the estimated rate of mental illness was particularly low among the Chinese group. For all outcomes except anxiety they had a lower detected rate than any other ethnic group, and for anxiety their detected rate was the second lowest, only being higher than that for the Bangladeshi group.

In contrast, the white minority group seemed to have the highest rates of mental illness. Their rates of anxiety, depression, suicidal thoughts and psychosis were not

---

1   At this point it is worth reconsidering the possibility that the instruments used did not perform well for the South Asian groups. If there were problems with the cross-cultural use of these instruments, exactly the pattern of findings just outlined would be expected. Both the Bangladeshi group and South Asian women would be expected to have had the lowest rates of identified mental illness compared to their white counterparts, because these groups were the least acculturated.

only higher than the rates for the white British group, but also higher than the rates for the other minority groups, although most of these differences were not statistically significant. However, differences between the white minority and Caribbean group were small. The interpretation of these findings is difficult. First, as just described, the performance of the instruments used to assess mental illness were not tested for this group. Second, the small number of respondents in this group makes it impossible to test which factors might have contributed to these high rates. Third, the white minority group was far from homogeneous. Although a large number of the respondents had Irish family origins, the details of the diverse origins of the others was unknown. Nevertheless, one implication is that factors associated with ethnic minority status might increase risk of mental illness regardless of skin colour.

Overview of socio-demographic factors contributing to a higher risk of mental illness

The tables, figures and models presented in Chapters 3 and 5 of this report also illustrate the factors that contributed to an individual's risk of mental illness in addition to ethnicity. In fact, the models in Chapter 5 suggest that these factors may make important contributions to ethnic variations in risk of mental illness. Nevertheless, the interpretation of such effects requires careful consideration for two reasons. First, only social class showed a relatively uniform effect across ethnic groups. As expected, the tables show that class was inversely related to mental health for all outcomes, with those in households without a full-time worker having the highest rates. In contrast, being married or cohabiting appeared to increase the risk of depression for the Caribbean group, while it reduced the risk for the white and South Asian groups. The fact that the association between demographic factors and risk of illness varied across ethnic groups in this way suggests that careful thought needs to be given as to what these variables actually represent.

Second, for a cross-sectional survey such as this causal direction cannot be determined with certainty. While we can assume that ethnic group membership precedes mental illness, the same cannot be said for marital status or class. For example, two contrasting hypotheses might be: that higher levels of social support available to the married protect them from mental illness; and that mental illness reduces the likelihood of getting married or increases the risk of marital breakdown. For social class there are two reasons why we can be slightly more confident in suggesting that the causal direction is from class to mental health in this study. First, the indicator of social class used here was not a measure of individual occupational status, but of the head of the household's, although the two will be highly related. This means that if the causal direction was from mental health to social class, as measured here, we would have to hypothesise that poor mental health in an adult in the household would affect the employment chances of other adults in the household. Second, there is growing acceptance that a poorer socio-economic position leads to an increased risk of a variety of health outcomes (Davey Smith *et al.*, 1990; Benzeval *et al.*, 1995; Department of Health, 1995). Given the range of health outcomes involved, it would be surprising if this were not the case for mental health as well.

IMPLICATIONS FOR FUTURE RESEARCH AND FOR POLICY

The complexity of the issues that this research has attempted to tackle and of the methodology that had to be adopted means that the work has inevitably raised as many questions as could be answered. Nevertheless, important messages for the future development of both research and policy arise from the work.

One of the most surprising findings in this study was the estimated rate of psychosis among Caribbeans. Contrary to previous research on rates of treatment, rates of psychosis were not elevated among Caribbean men in this study and were not elevated among young Caribbean men. And, while Caribbean women had twice the rate of psychosis compared with white women, this difference was not statistically significant and was not as high as expected. The first concern here must be to explore whether this finding is genuine, or a consequence of non-response to the survey. The similarity in patterns of non-response across age and gender for the different ethnic minority groups would suggest that the finding is genuine, but further community studies would help to clarify this issue. If the finding is genuine, the concern must be to explore the reasons for the over-representation of Caribbeans in psychiatric hospitals.

One possibility is that this is a consequence of misdiagnosis. Recent studies have used standardised instruments to assess patients (e.g. Harrison *et al.*, 1988) and findings from these indicate that Caribbean patients admitted with a psychotic disorder probably do meet the necessary criteria for such a diagnosis. This suggests that the issue is not one of misdiagnosis. However, some have suggested that the use of standardised instruments alone is not sufficient to elimate the risk of misdiagnosis in a cross-cultural study, because the cultural distance between the interviewer and respondent allows for misunderstanding and symptoms not being adequately examined (Brugha and Nayani, 1989). In order to eliminate this risk there is a need for ethnic matching of interviewer and respondent, as was done here.

A second possibility is that this is a result of differences in the ways that white and Caribbean patients are treated, with a focus on how and why the pathways that result in an admission to a psychiatric hospital might differ for Caribbean and white patients. There is a growing body of evidence that suggests that Caribbean patients are more likely to be treated coercively and that this might be inappropriate (Harrison *et al.*, 1989; McKenzie *et al.*, 1995; Davies *et al.*, 1996). Reasons for this need to explored at both a research and a policy level. In particular, it seems likely that this area would benefit from an exploration of what happens in primary care, because it is here that admissions to hospital and coercive treatment might be avoided.

However, if the three- to fivefold greater rates of treatment for psychosis among Caribbeans compared with whites were entirely due to differences in rates of detection and treatment, one would have to argue that the majority of white people with psychosis were going untreated. This is unlikely to be the case, and is also inconsistent with the similarity between the estimated general population prevalence of psychosis reported here and elsewhere. For example, if, as suggested by the data presented here, Caribbean men had the same rates of psychosis as white men, and all Caribbean men were treated, a threefold difference in treatment rates for Caribbean and white men would suggest that two-thirds of white men were not treated. This would imply that the estimated prevalence of psychosis among white men of 1 per cent reported here should be three times higher than a prevalence estimate based on treatment statistics.

Issues relating to primary care are also important for neurotic disorders. Findings presented in Chapter 3 indicate that the rate of neurotic disorders is high among the Caribbean group and that Caribbeans are just as likely as whites to consult with their GP about such problems, but they are less likely to receive medication. For the South Asian group the findings suggest that the rates of neurotic disorder presented in Chapter 3 may have been an underestimate and that this was a consequence of the failure of western psychiatric categories to identify mental illness across different cultures. However, this conclusion must be regarded as provisional and, although there is a growing body of evidence on this, further research needs to be undertaken. Particularly important here would be to undertake anthropological work aimed at improving our understanding of the ways in which different cultures express psychological distress. Such information is of great clinical significance. Clinical practice that is rooted in western concepts of mental illness may fail to identify illness among those with other cultural backgrounds. Consequently, practitioners, particularly at a primary care level where most neurotic illness is managed, need to be informed of possible differences in the presentation of illness and the forms that these differences might take. So, both the findings for the Caribbean and the South Asian groups suggest that practitioners at a primary care level need to be made more aware of the issues relating to the management of ethnic minority patients with a possible mental illness.

Elsewhere data from this survey (Nazroo, 1997) and from the work carried out by the Health Education Authority (Rudat, 1994) on the use made by ethnic minority people of primary care, have shown that the quality of the care received might be related to the ethnic background of the patient. Two issues seemed to be particularly important. One was the difficulties that ethnic minority people who were not fluent in English had with communicating with their doctor, difficulties that would no doubt aggravate cultural differences in the expression of illness. The second was related to the possibility that the geographical location of many ethnic minority people in inner-city areas might lead to them being more likely to use poorly resourced general practices. For example, one study contrasting inner London with other areas found that 46 per cent of inner London GP premises were below standard compared with 7 per cent of those in England as a whole (Jarman and Bosanquet, 1992). Both of these possibilities suggest that there should be some consideration of how to target resources more effectively at the facilities needed by those who provide services for ethnic minority groups

Finally, the findings presented in Chapter 5 of this report should be considered when attempting to understand the relationship between mental illness and ethnicity. Particularly important is that the rates of mental illness within particular ethnic groups varied greatly according to demographic and socio-economic indicators, and the differences between ethnic minority groups and whites were confined to sub-groups of the ethnic minority population. The implication is that differences in the rates of mental illness among different ethnic groups might not be a consequence of dimensions of ethnicity *per se,* such as culture or biology, but of the differences in the demographic and socio-economic profiles of different ethnic groups (Adebimpe, 1994).

References

American Psychiatric Association (1995) *Diagnostic and Statistical Manual IV.* Washington D.C.

Adebimpe, V.R. (1994) 'Race, racism, and epidemiological surveys', *Hospital and Community Psychiatry*, vol.45, no.1, pp.27–31

Ahmad, W. (1995) 'Review article: "Race" and health', *Sociology of Health and Illness*, vol.17, no.3, pp.418–429

Bagley, C. (1971) 'The social aetiology of schizophrenia in immigrant groups', International *Journal of Social Psychiatry*, vol.17, pp.292–304

Bebbington, P. & Nayani, T. (1995) 'The psychosis screening questionnaire', *International Journal of Methods in Psychiatric Research*, vol.5, pp.11–19

Benzeval, M., Judge, K. & Whitehead, M. (1995) *Tackling Inequalities in Health: An agenda for action.* London: King's Fund Institute

Biswas, S. (1990) 'Ethnic differences in self poisoning: a comparative study between an Asian and White adolescent group', *Journal of Adolescence*, vol.13, pp.189–193

Brown, C. and Ritche, J. (1981) *Focussed Enumeration: the development of a method for sampling ethnic minority groups.* London: Policy Studies Institute/SCPR

Bhugra, D., Hilwig, M., Hussein, B., Marceau, H., Neehall, J., Leff, J., Mallett, R & Der, G. (1996) 'First contact incidence rates of schizophrenia in Trinidad and one-year follow-up', *British Journal of Psychiatry*, vol.169, pp.587–592

Bughra, T. & Nayani, S. (1989) 'Language deficits – the handicapped interviewer or the handicapped patients', Paper presented at the Annual Meeting of the Royal College of Psychiatrists

Carpenter, L. & Brockington, I.F. (1980) 'A study of mental illness in Asians, West Indians and Africans living in Manchester', *British Journal of Psychiatry*, vol.137, pp.201–205

Cochrane, R. & Bal, S.S. (1989) 'Mental hospital admission rates of immigrants to England: a comparison of 1971 and 1981', *Social Psychiatry and Psychiatric Epidemiology*, vol.24, pp.2–11

Cochrane, R. & Sashidharan, S.P. (1996) 'Mental health and ethnic minorities: a review of the literature and implications for services'. In W. Ahmad, T. Sheldon & O. Stuart (eds) *Ethnicity and Health.* York: University of York

Cochrane, R. & Stopes-Roe, M. (1981) 'Psychological symptom levels in Indian immigrants to England – a comparison with native English', *Psychological Medicine*, vol.11, pp.319–327

Davey Smith, G., Bartley, M. & Blane, D. (1990) 'The Black report on socioeconomic inequalities in health 10 years on', *British Medical Journal*, vol.301, pp.373–377

Davies, S., Thornicroft, G., Leese, M., Higgingbotham, A. & Phelan, M. (1996) 'Ethnic differences in risk of compulsory psychiatric admission among representative cases of psychosis in London', *British Medical Journal*, vol.312, pp.533–537

Dean, G., Walsh, D., Downing, H., & Shelley, E. (1981) 'First admissions of native-born and immigrants to psychiatric hospitals in south-east England 1976', *British Journal of Psychiatry*, vol.139, pp.506–512

Department of Health (1995) *Variations in Health. What can the Department of Health and the NHS do?* London: Department of Health

Fenton, S. & Sadiq-Sangster, A. (1996) 'Culture, relativism and the expression of mental distress: South Asian women in Britain', *Sociology of Health and Illness*, vol.18, no.1, pp.66–85

Gilliam, S.J., Jarman, B., White, P. & Law, R. (1989) 'Ethnic differences in consultation rates in urban general practice', *British Medical Journal*, vol.299, pp.953–957

Glover, G.R. (1989) 'Why is there a high rate of schizophrenia in British Caribbeans?', *British Journal of Hospital Medicine*, vol.42, pp.48–51

Gordon, T (1982) 'Further mortality experience among Japanese Americans', *Public Health Reports*, vol.97, pp.973–984

Halpern, D. (1993) 'Minorities and mental health', *Social Science and Medicine*, vol.36, no.5 pp.597–607

Handy, S., Chithiramohan, R.N., Ballard, C.G. & Silveira, W.R. (1991) 'Ethnic differences in adolescent self-poisoning: a comparison of Asian and Caucasian groups', *Journal of Adolescence*, vol.14, pp.157–162

Harrison, G., Holton, A., Neilson, D., Owens, D., Boot, D. & Cooper, J. (1989) 'Severe mental disorder in Afro-Caribbean patients: some social, demographic and service factors', *Psychological Medicine*, vol.19, pp.683–696

Harrison, G., Owens, D., Holton, A., Neilson, D. & Boot, D. (1988) 'A prospective study of severe mental disorder in Afro-Caribbean patients', *Psychological Medicine*, vol.18, pp.643–657

Harvey, I., Williams, P., McGuffin, P. & Toone, B.K. (1990) 'The functional psychoses in Afro-Caribbeans', *British Journal of Psychiatry*, vol.157, pp.515–522

Hickling, F.W. (1991) 'Psychiatric hospital admission rates in Jamaica', *British Journal of Psychiatry*, vol.159, pp.817–821

Hickling, F.W. & Rodgers-Johnson, P. (1995) 'The incidence of first contact schizophrenia in Jamaica', *British Journal of Psychiatry*, vol.167, pp.193–196

Jadhav, S. (1996) 'The cultural origins of western depression', *International Journal of Social Psychiatry*, vol.42, no.4, pp.269–286

Jarman, B. & Bosanquet, N. (1992) 'Primary health care in London – changes since the Acheson report', *British Medical Journal*, vol.305, pp.1130–1133

Jenkins, R. (1986) *Racism in Recruitment.* Cambridge: Cambridge University Press

Karmi, G., Abdulrahim, D., Pierpoint, T. & McKeigue, P. (1994) *Suicide among Ethnic Minorities and Refugees in the UK.* London: North East & North West Thames Regional Health Authority

King, M., Coker, E., Leavey, G., Hoare, A. & Johnson-Sabine, E. (1994) 'Incidence of psychotic illness in London: comparison of ethnic groups', *British Medical Journal*, vol.309, pp.1115–9

Kleinman, A. (1987) 'Anthropology and Psychiatry: The Role of Culture in Cross-Cultural Research on Illness', *British Journal of Psychiatry*, vol.151, pp.447–454

Krause, I. (1989) 'Sinking heart: a Punjabi communication of distress', *Social Science and Medicine*, vol.29, no.4, pp.563–575

Lewis, G., Pelosi, A.J., Araya, R. & Dunn, G. (1992) 'Measuring psychiatric disorder in the community: a standard assessment for use by lay interviewers', *Psychological Medicine*, vol.22, pp.465–486

Lipsedge, M. (1993) 'Mental health: access to care for black and ethnic minority people'. In A. Hopkins & V. Bahl (eds) *Access to Health Care for People from Black and Ethnic Minorities*. London: Royal College of Physicians

Littlewood, R. (1992) 'Psychiatric diagnosis and racial bias: empirical and interpretative approaches', *Social Science and Medicine*, vol.34, no.2, pp.141–149

Littlewood, R. & Lipsedge, M. (1981) 'Accute psychotic reactions in Caribbean born patients', *Psychological Medicine*, 11, 303–318

Littlewood, R. & Lipsedge, M. (1988) 'Psychiatric illness among British Afro-Caribbeans', *British Medical Journal*, vol.296, pp.950–951

Lloyd, K. (1993) 'Depression and anxiety among Afro-Caribbean general practice attenders in Britain', *International Journal of Social Psychiatry*, vol.39, pp.1–9

MacCarthy, B. & Craissati, J. (1989) 'Ethnic differences in response to adversity: A community sample of Bangladeshis and their indigenous neighbours', *Social Psychiatry and Psychiatric Epidemiology*, vol.24, pp.196–201

McGovern, D. & Cope, R. (1987) 'First psychiatric admission rates of first and second generation Afro-Caribbeans', *Social Psychiatry*, vol.22, pp.139–149

McGovern, D., Hemmings, P., Cope, R. & Lowerson, A. (1994) 'Long-term follow-up of young Afro-Caribbean Britons and white Britons with a first admission diagnosis of schizophrenia', *Social Psychiatry and Psychiatric Epidemiology*, vol.29, pp.8–19

McKenzie, K., van Os, J., Fahy, T., Jones, P., Harvey, I., Toone, B. & Murray, R. (1995) 'Psychosis with good prognosis in Afro-Caribbean people now living in the United Kingdom', *British Medical Journal*, vol.311, pp.1325–8

McKenzie, K.J. & Crowcroft, N. (1994) 'Race, ethnicity, culture, and science', *British Medical Journal*, vol.309, pp.286–287

Meltzer, H., Gill, B. & Petticrew, M. (1994) *The Prevalence of Psychiatric Morbidity among Adults Aged 16–64 Living in Private Households*. London: HMSO

Meltzer, H., Gill, B., Petticrew, M. & Hinds, K. (1995) *The Prevalence of Psychiatric Morbidity among Adults Living in Private Households*. London: HMSO

Merrill, J. & Owens, J. (1986) 'Ethnic Differences in Self-poisoning: A Comparison of Asian and White Groups', *British Journal of Psychiatry*, vol.148, pp.708–712

Modood, T., Berthoud, R., Lakey, J., Nazroo, J., Smith, P., Virdee, S. & Beishon, S. (1997) *Ethnic Minorities in Britain: Diversity and Disadvantage*. London: Policy Studies Institute

National Association for the Care and Resettlement of Offenders, Mental Health Advisory Committee (1995) *Mentally Disturbed Prisoners*. London: NACRO

Nazroo, J.Y. (1997) *The Health of Britain's Ethnic Minorities: Findings from a national survey*. London: Policy Studies Institute

Office of Population Censuses and Surveys (1994) *Undercoverage in Great Britain (census user guide no. 58)*. London: HMSO

Owen, D. (1994) 'Spatial variations in ethnic minority groups populations in Great Britain', *Population Trends*, no.78, pp.23–33

Rack, P. (1982) *Race, Culture and Mental Disorder*. London: Tavistock

Rudat, K. (1994) *Black and Minority Ethnic Groups in Britain: Health and Lifestyles*. London: Health Education Authority

Sashidharan, S.P. (1993) 'Afro-Caribbeans and schizophrenia: the ethnic vulnerability hypothesis re-examined', *International Review of Psychiatry*, vol.5, pp.129–144

Sashidharan, S, & Francis, E. (1993) 'Epidemiology, ethnicity and schizophrenia'. In W.I.U. Ahmad (ed) *'Race' and Health in Contemporary Britain*. Buckingham: Open University Press

Senior, P.A. & Bhopal, R. (1994) 'Ethnicity as a variable in epidemiological research', *British Medical Journal*, vol.309, pp.327–330

Sheldon, T.A. & Parker, H. (1992) 'Race and ethnicity in health research', *Journal of Public Health Medicine*, vol.14, no.2, pp.104–110

Smaje, C. (1995) *Health, 'Race' and Ethnicity: Making Sense of the Evidence*. London: King's Fund

Smith, P. (1996) 'Methodological aspects of research amongst ethnic minorities', *Survey Methods Centre Newsletter*, vol.16, no.1, pp.20–21

Smith, P. & Prior, G. (1997) *The Fourth National Survey of Ethnic Minorities: Technical Report*. London: Social and Community Planning Research

Soni Raleigh, V. (1996) 'Suicide patterns and trends in people of Indian subcontinent and Caribbean origin in England and Wales', *Ethnicity and Health*, vol.1, no.1, pp.55–63

Soni Raleigh, V. & Balarajan, R. (1992) 'Suicide and self-burning among Indians and West Indians in England and Wales', *British Journal of Psychiatry*, vol.161, pp.365–368

Soni Raleigh, V., Bulusu, L. & Balarajan, R. (1990) 'Suicides Among Immigrants from the Indian Subcontinent', British Journal of Psychiatry, vol.156, pp.46–50

Sugarman, P.A. & Crauford, D. (1994) 'Schizophrenia in the Afro-Caribbean Community', *British Journal of Psychiatry*, vol.164, pp.474–480

Syme, S., Marmot, M., Kagan, H. & Rhoads, G. (1975) 'Epidemiologic studies of CHD and stroke in Japanese men living in Japan, Hawaii and California', *American Journal of Epidemiology*, vol.102, pp.477–480

Van Os, J., Castle, D.J., Takei, N., Der, G. & Murray, R.M. (1996) 'Psychotic illness in ethnic minorities: clarification from the 1991 census', *Psychological Medicine*, vol.26, pp.203–208

Virdee, S. (1995) *Racial Violence and Harassment*. London: Policy Studies Institute

Virdee, S (1997) 'Racial Harassment'. In T. Modood, R. Berthoud, J. Lakey, J.Nazroo, P. Smith, S. Virdee & S. Beishon, *Ethnic Minorities in Britain: Diversity and Disadvantage*. London: Policy Studies Institute

World Health Organisation (1992) *International Classification of Mental and Behavioural Disorders*. Geneva: World Health Organisation

Williams, R. (1993) 'Health and length of residence among South Asians in Glasgow: a study controlling for age', *Journal of Public Health Medicine*, vol.15, no.1, pp.52–60

Wing, J.K., Cooper, J.E. & Sartorius, N. (1974) *Measurement and Classification of Psychiatric Symptoms*. Cambridge: Cambridge University Press

Survey Methods

STRUCTURE OF THE FOLLOW-UP STUDY

The main aim of the follow-up study was (as described in Chapters 1 and 2) to assess the validity of the mental health measures used in the Fourth National Survey, which were contained within a structured interview. The aim was to include in the follow-up study all respondents whose answers suggested that they may *possibly* have a mental illness; these respondents would then undergo a detailed clinical interview.

Due to linguistic and cultural variations, it was considered essential that the clinical interviews should be carried out by psychiatric nurses or doctors ethnically- and language-matched to the respondents. Version 9 of the Present State Examination (PSE) (Wing *et al.*, 1974) was chosen for the psychiatric assessment in this interview as it had already been translated into most of the languages required.

The interview also included a structured questionnaire covering treatment and use of health services.

The design of the follow-up survey closely followed that of the National Psychiatric Morbidity Study (Meltzer *et al.*, 1995), although there are some important differences (discussed in Chapter 1).

SELECTION OF RESPONDENTS FOR FOLLOW-UP INTERVIEW

Respondents were screened in to the follow-up survey on the basis of their answers in the Fourth National Survey interview. The inclusion criteria were as wide as possible, in order to minimise the number of false negatives (i.e. respondents who had a mental illness, but were not identified for follow-up). Respondents were screened in according to their answers on either the CIS-R, or the PSQ, or because they stated that they took an antipsychotic medicine, or had a diagnosed psychiatric disorder. Because only half of the ethnic minority sample in the Fourth National Survey were asked the CIS-R (depression) screening questions, in order to give white and ethnic minority respondents and equal chance of being followed up only half of the white respondents who met the CIS-R criteria were approached for the follow-up interview. Full details of the screening criteria are given in Chapter 1.

In order to maximise response to the follow-up study, it was important to contact respondents for follow-up interview as soon as possible after they had completed the Fourth National Survey interview. To achieve this, answers to the screening questions were keyed as a separate exercise, as soon as the Fourth National Survey questionnaires were received in the office, rather than wait for batch keying of the questionnaires to be completed. This meant that the screening data were not edit-checked in advance of identification of cases for follow-up; subsequent edit-checking revealed a few cases where the unedited data were not correct, and cases for follow-up were mis-identified. Overall 24 respondents who did not meet the selection criteria were included in the follow-up.

Identification of cases for follow-up was carried out on a weekly basis, and names and addresses of screened-in respondents were issued to the field managers. Despite this, the demands of the process meant that there was on average a sizeable gap between the two interviews. The median gap was 17 weeks, and 80 per cent of follow-up interviews were done between 9 and 26 weeks after the first interview.

FIELDWORK PROCEDURES

Once a respondent had been identified for follow-up interview, the name and address was issued to an interviewer to make contact and arrange an appointment for follow-up. Wherever possible, the same interviewer who carried out the Fourth National Survey interview with the respondent was responsible for arranging the follow-up appointment, and introducing the nurse interviewer to the respondent.

To carry out the clinical interviews, PSI recruited a panel of psychiatric nurses and doctors who had appropriate language skills, and were ethnically-matched to the respondents. The psychiatric nurses and doctors received a week's training in the use of the PSE. After the interviewers had been trained in the use of the PSE, their reliability was assessed by asking them to rate a taped interview with a depressed and with a schizophrenic patient. The result of this exercise was satisfactory. (Further details are given in Chapter 2).

Fieldwork for the follow-up study took place between spring 1994 and spring 1995, lagging a couple of months behind the fieldwork for the Fourth National Survey, in order to allow time to carry out as many follow-up interviews as possible.

RESPONSE TO THE FOLLOW-UP STUDY

The net fieldwork response rate was 68 per cent; that is, follow-up interviews were achieved with 68 per cent of those respondents who were identified for follow-up. (It should be remembered that, because the identification process was carried out on un-edited data, there were a few cases where respondents were wrongly screened in to the follow-up survey, or wrongly screened out. This is discussed above.) Details are shown in Table A.1.

Table A.1   Response rates

	Number	Per cent
Addresses identified for follow-up	845	100
Unable to follow up (name of respondent missing etc)	9	1
Unproductive at interviewer visit:		
Address empty	4	*
Moved, not retraced	32	4
No contact	37	4
Refused	85	10
Other unproductive	19	2
Appointment made for nurse/doctor visit	659	78
Unproductive at nurse/doctor visit:		
Refusal	39	5
Broken appointment	37	4
Other reason	8	1
Productive nurse/doctor interview completed	575	68

Details of the number of white and ethnic minority respondents at each stage of the study are shown in Table A.2. It should be remembered that only half of the ethnic minority respondents were asked the depression screening questions, and that the number of achieved interviews at the validation stage were a reflection of both response rates and the number of respondents selected for follow-up. Reasons for not being selected for follow-up included: only half of the white sample who were identified as suitable for follow-up on the basis of the screening criteria for depression were actually approached for follow-up (see Chapter 2); because the screening was done on unedited data some respondents were misclassified on the screening criteria (see above); and some respondents indicated at the initial interview that they did not want to be involved in any further interviews, so were not approached.

Table A.2   Number of respondents at each stage of the study

	Neurotic depression		Psychosis	
	Minority respondents	Whites	Minority respondents	Whites
Underwent initial interview	5196	2867	5196	2867
Asked screening questions	2579	2867	5196	2867
Screened positive	349	485	287	171
Selected for follow-up	297	255	228	142
Successfully followed up	190	188	157	94

Tables and Figures

CHAPTER 4

CHAPTER 5

APPENDIX

Index

The Fourth National Survey of Ethnic Minorities

• **Lead title** •

ETHNIC MINORITIES IN BRITAIN
Diversity and Disadvantage

Tariq Modood, Richard Berthoud, Jane Lakey, James Nazroo, Patten Smith, Satnam Virdee and Sharon Beishon

The most comprehensive study available of the economic and social circumstances of Britain's ethnic minorities, in a series which has established itself as a key reference and required reading for all academics and policy makers involved in these issues.

This is the fourth in a series of major studies by the Policy Studies Institute which have charted the experiences of ethnic minorities in Britain since the 1960s. It reports on changes in such key fields as family structure, education, employment and housing. And it introduces new topics which have not been examined thoroughly in the past: poverty, health, racial harassment and cultural identity.

Ethnic Minorities in Britain is required reading for anyone concerned about multi-cultural Britain.

Contents: Foreword by Professor Bhikhu Parekh • Introduction • People, Families and Households • Qualifications and English Language • Employment • Income and Standards of Living • Neighbourhoods and Housing • Health and Health Services • Racial Harassment • Culture and Identity • Conclusion

£17.50, paperback, ISBN 0 85374 670 2
June 1997, 234x153mm, 440 pages

*PSI publications are available from Grantham Book Services Ltd
Isaac Newton Way, Alma Park Industrial Estate, Grantham, Lincs NG31 9SG
Orders: (Tel) 01476 541080 (Fax) 01476 541061*

The Fourth National Survey of Ethnic Minorities

• **Just published** •

THE HEALTH OF BRITAIN'S ETHNIC MINORITIES

James Nazroo

The most detailed examination of the health of Britain's ethnic minorities available – a key text for university courses on epidemiology, public health medicine, medical sociology and anthropology, and race relations.

The Fourth National Survey included an extensive section on health, health-related behaviours and the use of health services. This means that, for the first time, there has been an opportunity to explore the complex relationship between health and ethnicity using a sample that is fully representative of the ethnic groups included. The rich detail of the lives of members of different ethnic groups provided by the survey has also meant that factors which might explain the relationship between ethnicity and health could be directly considered.

Findings presented in the report challenge current assumptions about the uniform pattern of ill-health across broadly defined ethnic groups, such as 'South Asian'. They also illustrate the importance of socio-economic factors to differences in health, both within particular ethnic groups and when making comparisons across ethnic groups. Consequently, the report challenges the focus on culture and biology as key explanatory factors for ethnic variations in health, with important implications for policy and practice. It also raises important theoretical and methodological issues for research on ethnicity and health.

£14.95 paperback ISBN 0 85374 709 1
July 1997 234x153mm 224 pages

*PSI publications are available from Grantham Book Services Ltd
Isaac Newton Way, Alma Park Industrial Estate, Grantham, Lincs NG31 9SG
Orders: (Tel) 01476 541080 (Fax) 01476 541061*

CHANGING ETHNIC IDENTITIES

Tariq Modood, Sharon Beishon and Satnam Virdee

The British population includes over 3 million people with origins outside Europe. New cultures are taking root in and adapting to Britain, and as part of the new trend in 'identity politics', British race relations are increasingly being shaped by new forms of minority ethnic and religious assertiveness.

What are these new forms of identities? To what extent are they rooted in cultural difference? Or are they mainly a reaction to racism? Do different minority groups emphasise different aspects of their heritage, and how do they reconcile a commitment to those heritages with being British?

This book represents the first comparative study based on original fieldwork covering two generations of Caribbeans and the main South Asian groups on what their ethnic background means to them.It examines the basis of ethnic identity in family life, community languages, religion, marriage choices and in experiences of racial exclusion and forms of political solidarity. It highlights the changes that have taken place and are taking place between the migrant and British-born generation, and challenges those who think in terms of the simplistic oppositions of British–Alien or Black–White.

The authors conclude that we need a new view of Britishness and the varieties and forms that it can encompass, a Britishness which allows minorities to make a claim upon it, and to be accepted without having to conform to a narrow cultural norm.

£15.00 paperback ISBN 0 85374 646 X
1995 229x145mm 144 pages

PSI publications are available from Grantham Book Services Ltd
Isaac Newton Way, Alma Park Industrial Estate, Grantham, Lincs NG31 9SG
Orders: (Tel) 01476 541080 (Fax) 01476 541061

RACIAL VIOLENCE AND HARASSMENT

Satnam Virdee

Serious attacks on African Caribbean and South Asian people have made racial violence and harassment an issue of widespread public concern.

Any useful discussion of how racial violence and harassment should be tackled needs to be based on a thorough understanding of the nature and scale of the problem. The official figures on the extent of racial violence and harassment in Britain are based on police statistics and the British Crime Survey. This book offers a critical evaluation and assessment of these sources to see if the problem has, as some claim, increased. The report reviews a number of small-scale studies in local areas where racial violence and harassment is known to be a problem. Detailed questioning about the experience of racial violence and harassment -- particularly 'low-level' harassment -- among a sample of African Caribbean and South Asian respondents then reveals:

- where such incidents take place;
- who the perpetrators are;
- what, if anything, the people subject to such violence and harassment try to do about it; and
- the extent to which people's lives are affected, beyond the actual harassment that takes place.

The report concludes with a discussion of the key issues involved in addressing the problem more effectively.

£9.95 paperback ISBN 0 85374 647 8
1995 229x145mm 96 pages

PSI publications are available from Grantham Book Services Ltd
Isaac Newton Way, Alma Park Industrial Estate, Grantham, Lincs NG31 9SG
Orders: (Tel) 01476 541080 (Fax) 01476 541061

• Student text •

BRITAIN'S ETHNIC MINORITIES

Trevor Jones

Research in the 1960–1980s showed that Britain's ethnic minority population had substantially lower living standards than white people. Since then, of course, Britain has experienced major social and economic restructuring. *Britain's Ethnic Minorities* is an examination of how such changes have been reflected in the social and economic circumstances of ethnic minority groups.

Drawing on the Labour Force Survey and other comparative data, the book includes an extensive analysis of the labour market position of the main ethnic minority groups. It covers population size and geographical location; age and family structure; labour force participation; industrial distribution; job levels; trade union membership; unemployment; job search; and patterns of tenure. A key theme is the growing diversity within and between different ethnic minority groups, as some make greater progress than others into education and the labour market.

This book provides a comprehensive introduction to the socio-economic position of Britain's ethnic minorities. It will be of considerable interest to teachers and students of sociology, social policy and politics.

£9.95 paperback ISBN 0 85374 684 2
1996 229x145mm 192 pages

PSI publications are available from Grantham Book Services Ltd
Isaac Newton Way, Alma Park Industrial Estate, Grantham, Lincs NG31 9SG
Orders: (Tel) 01476 541080   (Fax) 01476 541061

NURSING IN A MULTI-ETHNIC NHS

Sharon Beishon, Satnam Virdee and Ann Hagell

Approximately 8 per cent of National Health Service nursing and midwifery staff are from ethnic minority groups. This major study of the careers of nurses and midwives found large gaps between equal opportunity policies on the one hand, and actual practices in the workplace on the other.

Drawing conclusions from both a qualitative study of six nurse employers and 150 interviews, and a nationally representative postal survey of over 14,000 staff, the book shows that many ethnic minority and white nurses felt that the allocation of training and promotion opportunities was unfair, that racial harassment of ethnic minority nursing staff by patients and colleagues was widespread, that management was not doing enough to tackle the problem of racial harassment and that they were forced to accept it as 'part of the job'. Moreover, some groups of ethnic minority nurses, in particular black nurses, had not advanced a far up the grading structure as their white colleagues.

This study reveals significant gaps between written policies and nurses' experiences which need to be addressed, and discusses the policy implications behind these findings.

£24.95 paperback ISBN 0 85374 662 1
1995 229x145mm 320 pages

*PSI publications are available from Grantham Book Services Ltd
Isaac Newton Way, Alma Park Industrial Estate, Grantham, Lincs NG31 9SG
Orders: (Tel) 01476 541080   (Fax) 01476 541061*

The Fourth National Survey of Ethnic Minorities

ASIAN SELF-EMPLOYMENT

The interaction of culture and economics in England

Hilary Metcalf, Tariq Modood and Satnam Virdee

Self-employment has grown disproportionately among South Asians. Today one third of Asian men in paid employment are self-employed, compared to one fifth of white men. In some parts of the UK, Asian businesses are expanding more rapidly than those of any other group. Yet these positive trends mask a more complex and less optimistic picture than is commonly painted. There are sharp differences in levels of business success between various groups in the Asian community, and indications suggest that the remarkable growth seen over recent decades is losing its momentum, as the first generation British Asians encourage their children to move into professional and salaried careers.

This unique study offers, for the first time, a detailed comparison of different Asian communities, and challenges the common assumption that all Asian groups can be regarded as the same. Among its findings it identifies:

- ways in which culture and religion could impact on entry into self-employment;
- how negative factors such as racism at work and 'dead-end jobs' have led to increased levels of self-employment;
- barriers to success in business, and how specific problems are more prevalent among specific Asian groups;
- the need to target assistance; and
- evidence that Asian self-employment may not continue at its currently high rates.

£14.95 paperback ISBN 0 85374 698 2
November 1996 216x135mm 128 pages

*PSI publications are available from Grantham Book Services Ltd
Isaac Newton Way, Alma Park Industrial Estate, Grantham, Lincs NG31 9SG
Orders: (Tel) 01476 541080 (Fax) 01476 541061*

• **Just published** •

CREDIT USE AND ETHNIC MINORITIES

Alicia Herbert and Elaine Kempson

Britain's ethnic minorities who live on low incomes are likely to have a high level of need for credit – a need which is often unmet by high-street banks and building societies.

This is the first available assessment of the ways in which members of these communities find and use credit. The authors have made detailed case studies of Bangladeshi, Pakistani and Afro-Caribbean communities to present a unique guide to patterns of credit use among ethnic minorities and the ways in which these patterns vary from the wider picture among low-income households. Using extensive desk research, consultations with community leaders and over 50 in-depth interviews, they give a clear account of:

- attitudes to credit, the need for credit, and the range of sources available and used;
- the extent to which people have access to the high-street credit market, and the barriers that prevent further access;
- levels of use of local credit markets, such as moneylenders and pawnbrokers, and the associated costs;
- the nature and extent of unlicensed credit markets within specific ethnic minority communities, and the need for legislation to protect vulnerable groups from these markets;
- the types of 'informal' responses which ethnic minority groups have devised, how they work, the extent and purpose of their use, and the costs and opportunities associated with them; and
- how such community initiatives might be encouraged so as to widen the choice of credit sources.

This is essential reading for those working in the credit markets, as well as for those involved in issues of race and ethnicity.

£9.95 paperback ISBN 0 85374 695 8
1996 216x135mm 128 pages

PSI publications are available from Grantham Book Services Ltd
Isaac Newton Way, Alma Park Industrial Estate, Grantham, Lincs NG31 9SG
Orders: (Tel) 01476 541080   (Fax) 01476 541061

• New •

CHURCH, STATE AND RELIGIOUS MINORITIES

Edited by Tariq Modood

The relationship between religion and state has not been a major issue for over a century. Yet the development of a new multicultural and multi-state situation in Britain is once again opening up some old constitutional debates, in particular about 'establishment', the privileged position of the Church of England in the British state. The Prince of Wales' highly publicised remark about not wanting to be 'Defender of the Faith' but a 'Defender of Faith' has now dramatically brought the question of the implications of recent multi-faith developments for establishment, the monarchy and British national identity to the centre of public attention.

This collection of essays, covering a range of faiths and secular views, explores these issues and the public role of religion in a plural society. The introduction provides an overview of the debate. Part One explores the issue in relation to concepts such as citizenship, equality, secularism and national identity. In Part Two, 'establishment' is defended and rejected by Christians and secular critics, while Part Three gives the perspectives of leading members of different minority faiths.

These thought-provoking chapters from prominent members of Jewish, Sikh, Buddhist, Muslim and Hindu communities, as well as Christian churches and varieties of secular opinion, make this the first book to explore the church–state relationship in Britain through focusing on the concerns of minority faiths.

£10.95 paperback ISBN 0 85374 724 5
May 1997 216X135mm 120 pages

PSI publications are available from Grantham Book Services Ltd
Isaac Newton Way, Alma Park Industrial Estate, Grantham, Lincs NG31 9SG
Orders: (Tel) 01476 541080   (Fax) 01476 541061